Praise for *Beyond the Morning Huddle*

"As a dental-employment law text, Dr. Ann Marie Gorczyca's *Beyond the Morning Huddle* provides a wonderful blend of law, dental environments and real stories that make it an easy read and educational at the same time."

– Arthur Curley, Attorney, Bradley, Curley & Asiano

"I find *Beyond the Morning Huddle* to be a breath of fresh air. Here, Dr. Ann Marie Gorczyca provides sensible, practical HR advice and delivers it in a way that is easy to read and to follow. Any practicing dentist who reads this book will take away many valuable tools for improving how they handle the often-tricky aspects of HR management in the running of their dental practice."

– David Harris, MBA, CMA, CFE, CFF, CEO Prosperident

"Many doctors look at staff as an expense, rather than as an asset. *Beyond the Morning Huddle* offers practical, easy-to-implement solutions to motivate staff to higher levels of performance while educating doctors on key employment laws to avoid costly liability. It's a complete guide to effective human resource management that no doctor should be without."

– John K. McGill, CPA, JD, MBA

"*Beyond the Morning Huddle* takes you through a real-world step-by-step process of what to do when faced with the most difficult and most often recurring HR problems that occur in a dental office. Dr. Gorczyca shares real-world guidance on what you can and should do in each instance. I commend Dr. Gorczyca for writing this book and taking the time to share her knowledge as an owner, doctor, and HR manager of her own team."

– Paul Edwards, Co-founder, CEDR Solutions

"Dr. Ann Marie Gorczyca's new book *Beyond the Morning Huddle* gives "true crime" scenarios found in the everyday world of dental practice. Each situation is common, and the names are changed so that these individuals might find employment in yet another dental office. This book is both entertaining and educational. It's also necessary. You'll find someone you know, either past or present, among the pages. Pick up this book for a great new approach to human resource management. What you'll find in this book is perspective: first that your dental office isn't *that* different, and second, that if you are faced with some of the circumstances outlined, there really are solutions. For real HR guidance, this book is a must read!"

– Wayne D Pernell, PhD, High-Performance Leadership Coach

"We have had the privilege of working with dentists since 1993 and now have over 600 dental clients nationwide. Within this context I can say that Dr. Ann Marie Gorczyca is one of the few dentists that really "gets it" when it comes to human resources and the critical necessity of having a solid HR structure in place. I am very happy she has written this book from a dentist's perspective and I know it will be helpful for so many of her colleagues."

– Barbara Freet, PHR, President, Human Resource Advisors

"This book is a must read for all dentists and recent grads who want to discover that the secret of a successful practice begins with a great dental team. Most employment lawsuits can be avoided with the nuggets of information and real-world examples found in this book. I would recommend this book to every client."

– Ali Oromchian, Esq. Dental and Medical Counsel

"*Beyond the Morning Huddle* is well-organized, accessible, and easy to read, and contains quality content while describing real-world applicable HR experience. In short, I like it!"

– Howard Farran, DDS, MBA. *Dentaltown Magazine*

"After 25 years of clinical teaching of registered dental assistants, I find *Beyond the Morning Huddle* an extremely pertinent and timely book. The diverse case studies relate and explore common situations in everyday dental practice. In our ever-changing world, this unique book will keep you in the forefront of HR management. This is a must read to enhance and grow a healthy practice."

– Linda Bartolomucci Boyd, Professor, Diablo Valley College,
Author of *Dental Instruments: A Pocket Guide*

"Dr. Gorczyca has written a book about how to motivate, train, and inspire your team, which includes everything necessary and important for a successful professional and personal life in the dental field. She takes you through case studies which demonstrate how dental professionals handle hiring, training of new team members, teamwork, and work-life balance. You will find many "pearls of wisdom" in *Beyond the Morning Huddle* that will help you reach your practice goals more quickly and predictably. Dr. Gorczyca's book is a welcomed and needed resource for all of us in the dental profession who strive for personal and professional success and happiness."

– Dr. Donna Galante, Orthodontist, The Galante Group

"Dr. Gorczyca gives an inside look into the HR management of employees in a dental practice. Every day I help dentists properly document performance and manage their dental teams while minimizing their HR liability. I am recommending "Beyond the Morning Huddle" to all of my doctors. This book will be helpful to any dentist looking to start, grow, or manage their dental practice."

– Andrew Llama, HR for Health

Beyond the Morning
HUDDLE

HR Management
for a Successful Dental Practice

DR. ANN MARIE GORCZYCA

AUTHORITY
PUBLISHING

Beyond the Morning Huddle
HR Management for a Successful Dental Practice
By Ann Marie Gorczyca

1. MED 016090 Medical: Dentistry - Practice Management
2. MED 016000 Medical: Dentistry - General
3. BUS 043000 Business & Economics: Marketing - Genera

ISBN-10: 1935953680
ISBN-13: 978-1-935953-68-5

Cover design by Lewis Agrell
Interior design by JETLAUNCH

Printed in the United States of America

Authority Publishing
11230 Gold Express Dr. #310-413
Gold River, CA 95670
800-877-1097
www.AuthorityPublishing.com

To my mother, Stasia,
    daughter, sister, wife,
    principal, manager,
    mother, mentor, friend.

She understood people
    and how to bring out
    the best in them.

CONTENTS

FOREWORD

BY BRUCE TULGAN

Since the early 1990s, I've been advising business leaders in organizations of all shapes and sizes on how to leverage talent to meet their business objectives. That includes many, many organizations in the business of healthcare delivery. Here is a piece of advice for anyone in a position of leadership at any level in a dental practice (or really any medical office) of any size: Buy a copy of *Beyond the Morning Huddle* by Dr. Ann Marie Gorczyca, read it, and then buy a copy for every professional, every hiring manager, recruiter, HR professional, and anyone else in a position of supervisory responsibility in your practice. Why? Because this book offers a systematic approach to every aspect of human capital management you need to know to attract and select new team members, get them on board and up to speed more quickly and effectively, establish clear ground rules, and attend to all the basics of performance management. Not only that, but this book will help you do all that, not just within the bounds of legal and regulatory requirements and fairness, but also provides the wisdom of experience that will help you bring out the best in your employees, your organization, and yourself as a leader.

I love this book because, like my own work, it is a journey through one real-life case study after another. This evidence-based approach to human capital management offers success story after success story, as well as many pitfalls to live through vicariously and learn from without having to suffer the consequences yourself. I know that I, for one, will never experience a visit to my dentist ever again without reflecting on the many illuminating stories in this book.

Managing human capital is difficult and involves a lot of complexities:

- People come and go. So you are always losing good people. And you are always trying to get new people on board and up to speed. On top of that, one great employee is worth more than three or four or five mediocre employees. Sometimes you have to go to great lengths to effectively reward, retain, and develop the very best employees.

- Change regularly forces rework, often involving lots of moving parts, and therefore lots of counterparts here, there and everywhere.

- Most people must rely on many others within and without their immediate work group in order to do their own work.

- Everybody is trying nowadays to do more with less. Often you probably find yourself trying to do your jobs with what you may feel are insufficient resources.

- Human beings have weaknesses as well as strengths. Not only that, but everybody has bad days. Some people have bad weeks, months, and years. Productivity and quality of work are highly variable, sometimes due to employee performance. On top of all that, humans have attitudes, and not always good ones.

This book will help you anticipate, plan for, and navigate through all of these complexities. Don't get me wrong. There are very few new-fangled ideas in this book. But newfangled ideas are the last thing most leaders of dental or medical practices need when it comes to mastering human capital management. I promise you, what's missing in most practices is the rigorous and consistent practice of the fundamentals.

When leaders in professional services firms do not practice the fundamentals, the consequences are significant and costly: 1, you will be more likely to make suboptimal hiring decisions; 2, new hires will be more likely to get on-board and up to speed more slowly; 3, employees will have lower productivity and make more mistakes; 4, employees will be more likely to have negative attitudes as well as more conflicts with each other; 5, employees will be less likely to learn new technical skills and also less likely to improve in their non-technical skills; and 6, high-performers will be more likely to leave.

On the other hand, when leaders practice the fundamentals with rigor and consistency, everything goes much better: 1, you will hire better people; 2, they will get on-board and up to speed more quickly and effectively; 3, employees will do more work better and faster; 4, employees will have higher morale and therefore manifest much better attitudes; 5, employees will be more likely to learn and grow on an ongoing basis in technical skills as well as soft skills; and, 6, you will be much better able to push out the low performers and retain the high performers.

This book is a rock-solid guide to practicing the fundamentals of human capital management with rigor and consistency. In short, that is the business case for reading this book and then re-reading it and then keeping a copy on your desk for quick reference every step of the way.

Bruce Tulgan is the founder of RainmakerThinking, Inc.˚ and the author of numerous books including *It's Okay to Be the Boss* (2007), *Not Everyone Gets a Trophy* (2009), and *The 27 Challenges Managers Face* (2014).

INTRODUCTION

*Either write something worth reading or
do something worth writing.*
– Benjamin Franklin

When I ask a fellow dentist "How are things at your office?" frequently we discuss an employee personnel situation. The dentist may be distraught. Often, they are burdened by an HR problem and wondering what to do to find a peaceful solution.

There is no aspect of dental practice that is more difficult or daunting than human resource management (HRM). Personally challenging and often emotionally charged, HRM may be something dentists wish to avoid, but they cannot. For *everyone* running a successful dental practice, HRM is a critical element of the business-management mix.

When it comes to HRM and dentists, I've seen macho men go to court, strong women cry, and capable team members pursue outrageous activities. I've also seen joy, career development, and the great teamwork of outstanding dental professionals working together to have the best workplace days of their lives.

Human resource management encompasses all aspects of the human condition. Why then are we surprised when we experience this broad spectrum of human behaviors in our place of employment, the dental office?

HRM can frustrate dentists and literally drive them to the edge. They may think they no longer want to run or own their dental office. It is easy for the dental business owner to sometimes feel that there is no solution to their HR problem and that they are alone. This is especially true when it comes to HRM and difficult interpersonal situations. There is a solution to every HR problem. It's important to focus on the performance and not the person, and be able to recognize desirable and undesirable work behaviors in order to know how to surround yourself with positive, productive team members. It's also important to know when to take HRM action, and what action to take.

Every dentist's dream is to eliminate day-to-day HRM issues and focus on optimal dental patient care. The last thing that a new patient should ever experience in the dental office is an atmosphere of tension. An outstanding dental team will work well together, and ultimately delight patients, producing dental-practice success. To do that, dentists need to get HRM right.

To some dental leaders, the HRM skills enabling teamwork and performance come naturally. For others, HRM needs to be reviewed for best practices and acquisition of HR knowledge and wisdom. To those who need to work on their HRM leadership skills, the information in this book will be helpful.

As a child, I first learned of HRM from my mother, an elementary-school principal for over 32 years. Often, I observed her preparation of the daily, weekly, and annual tasks of HRM. She meticulously reviewed the performance of each teacher, praised them for achievements and outlined individual goals and areas of improvement for the coming year. She also held an annual party for her team at our home. Regarding one teacher, whose behavior was unprofessional and performance substandard, I remember the steps of well-planned and legal termination. This wasn't easy—but it was necessary. Such an issue may also be the case for you, in your dental practice. You may need to dismiss an Undesirable Work Behavior team member to eliminate office disturbance, prevent liability, maintain team morale, or just to be able to sleep a little better at night.

When I was a student at the Harvard School of Dental Medicine, I had the opportunity to study at Harvard School of Public Health in the Department of Health Management and Policy. There, I attended my first health-organization management lectures and started to understand the importance and broad-reaching effects of HRM within the health-care field of dentistry. This perspective can be valuable to you, the dental professional, in the management of your business, your dental practice.

When I started teaching at the University of the Pacific's Arthur A. Dugoni School of Dentistry in the orthodontic Practice Management Course, I struggled with how I would convey to the orthodontic residents all aspects of HRM. Aiming to always to remain positive and encouraging, I searched for a title for my HRM presentation. "The Joy of Human Resource Management" came to mind as a noble goal. This is the end that we can all work towards. This book will describe the means.

THE MORNING HUDDLE

Do you have a morning huddle? Comprising approximately 10 minutes per workday, the morning huddle may be the best part of HR management for the day. It's *after* the morning huddle that dentists need to have courage, conversations, and candor in order to produce HR management performance results.

Human resource management goes far beyond the morning huddle. Organizational health can't be improved by a single huddle, outing, a retreat, a group hug, a magic wand, or singing "Kumbaya." HRM requires education, organization, and implementation. HRM mastery demands time, attention, and a team working together to produce trust, commitment, communication, accountability, results, and excellence. Your dental team cannot read your mind. HRM will require one-on-one communication and coaching.

We are fortunate in dentistry to have the opportunity to run our own small business and experience workplace freedom. Like some of you, I started an orthodontic office from scratch. At first, I had few workplace benefits. I was new and unknown to the community. Early on, I picked new hires from a small supply of applicants. As resources increased, I was able to offer career development and add devoted dental professionals to my own dental team. Some have stayed for decades, others only a few months. As my office grew, the team changed. Dedicated and loyal team members developed and became stakeholders. Undedicated and low performers left. We began active recruiting, and built a capable dental team of motivated professionals. We now enjoy practicing in an "A+ office culture."

Dentistry is a service industry. Those who choose to enter it need to have an attitude of service in their human nature. Some team members are keepers, and some need to be removed from the dental employment pool. Even ideal team members are not perfect, but they understand people, teamwork, stress management, and a successful blend of work-life balance. Exceptional team members are self-aware, emotionally intelligent, and work their personal best each day. They are a pleasure to work with and they make each and every day at the dental office fun.

Dental office environments may differ, but people are people. We will always have a challenge of working together closely in perfect harmony. The principles of HR management are universal, with legal guidelines. What's important is to create an office culture of performance, teamwork, and happiness while remembering that the dental patient is the ultimate boss. For a successful dental practice, HR policies will need to be followed. It is paramount that these rules are clearly presented in a professionally prepared, legally compliant, policy and procedures manual—your Team Handbook. This manual, your Team Handbook, is the foundation of your human resource management.

How DO you deal with bad attitudes and undesirable work behaviors in the dental office? When you consciously play by the HRM rules, good guys win, bad guys go home. It takes HR wisdom, courage, and action to get the job done. HR wisdom is having good judgment. Good judgment comes from HR experience. HR experience comes from studying, understanding, and learning from bad judgment.

This book contains fifty-two case studies of HRM situations with solutions. You may experience several of these scenarios over the course of your dental career. The names and people are not real but the situations are real and have been experienced and shared among members of the dental community. Add these situations to your experience and you will have gained 25 years of HRM wisdom.

HRM challenges are ever-present. I hope that these case studies will be helpful to you, especially those of you just starting out who are "a little green" with inexperience and may need HRM help, some encouragement, a positive push towards action, or a "you-are-not-alone" confirmation to make you feel empowered. This book will also be useful to dentists at mid-career and beyond who may need to be reminded to make positive attitude and performance a team requirement as well as having fun. Yes, fun! The more you make HRM a team sport, the more fun you will have.

HRM includes Recruitment, Integration, Management, Behaviors, Employment Law, Distribution of Resources, and Leadership. A proactive and organized approach to HRM will have costs in terms of both time and money. Avoiding or ignoring HRM challenges would be costlier. Mastering HRM will be priceless.

Successful HRM is the key to your personal and professional happiness as a dental professional. Creating an "A+ work culture" will lead to thriving patients. Doing HRM right will help you conquer your challenges and create the dental practice of your dreams.

Now, let's get started.

HOW TO USE THIS BOOK

The head of human resources at every company
should be at least as important as the CFO.
                                    – Jack Welch, CEO, General Electric

What is human resource management? HRM is everything you do that has anything to do with the employment of your dental team. Everything counts and must be done in accordance with state and federal employment law. This book outlines the six keys areas of HRM.

Human Resource Management can be divided into six main categories:

I.   Recruitment – The hiring process.
II.   Integration – Welcoming, training, and placement of the new team member.
III. HR Management – Leading an efficient, effective, and happy team.
IV.   Feedback – Performance reviews.
V.   Distribution of Resources – Payroll, bonuses, and benefits.
VI.   Employment Law – Having rules and playing by them.

To explain these activities, I have written fifty-two case studies taken from true experiences and histories from my private orthodontic practice in Antioch, California, dental colleagues' private offices, as well as account histories shared by dental advisors, mentors, and friends in the dental and HR industry. Included here also is HRM insight gained through my involvement in dental-business management education and experience spanning 30 years. Included are good practices to consider, as well as mistakes to avoid.

Every day, there is a new question.
– Jack Welch

All dentists work in a business within the healthcare industry. We need an efficient, effective, and professional team to deliver our product: dental health. The implementation of all HRM requires knowledge, organization, and leadership.

An ultimate work goal is to create and enjoy the best dental team possible in the best work environment. Once you understand how HRM fits into your dental practice, and the challenges and responsibilities of HRM, you will move one step closer to HRM success.

Each day, you strive to restore your patients to ideal dental health. Accompanying you on this journey is your dental team. You may be spending more time with your dental team than with your own spouse and family. You want your team to be the best it can possibly be. This is done by team-member selection and management. In the growth and health of your dental practice, HRM is a key element of the business-management mix.

As you read the HRM stories presented in this book, you will be able to construct your own 12-month HR calendar (a copy can be found in the appendix). Plan the items from each of the book's six parts: Recruitment, Integration, HR Management, Feedback, Employment Law, and Distribution of Resources. Write the date of project initiation on the calendar. See them through to completion. Once you have launched your human resource management plan, keep track of your results on a daily basis in a small notebook. Meet with each team member daily, even if only to ask, "How are you?" and, "How is your work going today?" Once you have reviewed and analyzed your results, take action. Eliminate the hazards and replace them with assets. *Be courageous. Hold conversations. Have candor.*

Part One

RECRUITMENT

Hiring good people is hard.
Hiring great people is brutally hard.
– Jack Welch

T he only one sure thing in life is change, so be in a state of constant preparedness. Recruitment is an active ongoing process. If you meet someone great in the dental industry, or any industry for that matter, whom you feel would be a great addition to your dental team, ask for their resume and keep it on file for the day that you have a new job opening. If you have a high school or dental intern whom you love and know does great work, keep their personnel file on hand after their term in your office is over and keep in touch. If someone tells you that they would love to work in your office, ask them to submit their resume. This could be a former patient, parent or relative of a patient, friends of your team members, visitors or friendly individuals known in your local community. This is "active recruitment."

Active recruitment of great people whom you already know is far more successful than a random hit of a cold interview of a stranger. Keep as many good references in your active recruitment file as possible. This will give you a great start for the time when you have a new personnel need and a job opening to fill.

Active recruitment of new hires is often done by existing team members. If they know someone whom they trust and respect looking for a new job, they will ask their friend and colleague to drop by your office for a Meet and Greet or to fill out a job application. Desirable and experienced dental professionals exhibit emotional intelligence and good workplace behaviors. These positive people willingly help others, volunteer to complete tasks, take initiative on projects, happily share the workload, assist the doctor, make suggestions on how to improve the office, are punctual, have excellent attendance, like their teammates, and have an excellent attitude.

To quickly discover those looking for a new job, you may place an ad for a new hire on Craigslist. If so, you will receive dozens of resumes from applicants who may not be qualified for your job. Be aware that many of the worst employees who have been terminated are on Craigslist.

Be as specific as you can with the job-opening announcement. Read between the lines of the resumes that you receive to quickly eliminate those with worries and select those with promise. Selection for neatness, accurate spelling, work longevity, good GPA, great attendance, and references listed are a good place to start.

Junior colleges are also an excellent place to announce a dental job opening. Dental assistant programs and business programs can link dentists directly to recent graduates looking for a job as well as give references and recommendations.

Should you hire a recruitment agency headhunter? Professional headhunters might call local dental offices and ask to speak with the person in the job which you have open to fill. They aim to lure the team member on the phone away from their present office with an increased dollar offer or more benefits. These calls, if effective, can destroy existing dental office teams and can destabilize your team as well. They sow seeds of discontent as part of their otherwise quite legitimate business.

Occasionally, an HR firm may present a legitimate person who is unhappy at their present job or has contacted the agency themselves looking for a new job. Be sure to ask the agency how they acquired the proposed candidate. Be sure to ask why the person they have found left their last dental office job. Then call for references.

Hiring a new team member is usually not easy. You will need to devote time and attention to the hiring process. You will need excellent interview skills and scripted questions. You will benefit from working interviews and making careful observations and taking notes. Watch your candidate take a message, handwrite a note, or file reports. Watch if they are fast or slow. See if they can "shift gears" to a new task readily.

You will be surprised what people know and do not know.

Assessments are a great tool for giving you more information quickly about a candidate. The DISC Personality Test outlining Dominance, Influence, Steadiness, and Conscientiousness is one such resource. Results will give you insight into the personality traits, behavioral patterns, and instinctual reactions of the candidate. Other questionnaires evaluate work ethic, reliability, teamwork, or problem solving. These are all desirable attributes to improve your dental office and dental team.

The Job Related Assessment Test is certified for work trades. This evaluates behavioral style, core convictions, and compatibility. Made known here are the candidate's ambitions, beliefs, compassion and discipline. For more information on assessment tests, contact Barbara Freet, Human Resource Advisors at www.humanresourceadvisors.com.

Chapter 1

NEW TEAM MEMBERS

A smile is
the universal welcome.
— Max Eastman

How do you find exceptional new hires? Where do you look? What do you look for? Are you swayed by good looks in hiring attractive new dental assistants to "WOW" your patients? Or are you looking for a hardworking, honest, cheerful person with good performance histories and a great teamwork attitude? Do you make integrity a top priority? Do you evaluate your gut feeling of who is trustworthy or whom you like? Will this new person grow professionally as your practice grows?

Evaluation of character traits and attributes beyond first impressions will take time to evaluate. Whether you get what you want in a new hire will depend on your interview skills and how hard and long you look for that which you seek. There may already be someone available in the resumes that you have been actively collecting who is a perfect fit for your job and your dental team.

Successful avenues for new hires include hiring college interns. Those who have completed educational rotations in your office and who you have already trained and screened, and are liked, accepted, trusted, and respected by your present team. Graduated dental assisting interns are perhaps the best and most hassle-free new hires.

A second source for great new hires is direct referral from trusted friends, relatives, and colleagues of your office. A third creator of experienced new hires is extraordinary circumstances, such as a new home move, office financial cutback, or voluntary resignation from an unreasonable or "hostile" dental office.

In my experience, the least effective approach to finding a new hire is placement of a cold ad on Craigslist. If you must search via placement services, try DentalPost at www.dentalpost.net. Clinical positions can be listed in the dental section. A front-office position can be listed in the business section as well as the dental section. To avoid wasting the time on inappropriate applicants, *specify the pay range in your job ads.* This will save you time by not attracting those overqualified for your dental office position.

Beyond attitude and skill, the sincere desire to want to work in your office is half of the new-recruitment puzzle. Office integration is the other half.

In general, promoting from within your dental office to fill higher-level positions is a way of encouraging personal career development and promotion. Your present team members often know good people looking for new dental office employment. They may be former schoolmates or assistants from offices where they may have formerly worked. Personal referrals are often safe and successful hires. They are also cost-effective.

CASE STUDY 1: "THE NEW HIRE"

Having suffered the death of a close uncle, dental assistant Annie requested one week off to attend his out-of-state funeral. Her request for leave was denied. She told her boss of over seven years that this funeral was very important to her and that she must attend it even if this meant being written up or losing her job. Her employer stated "fine," then terminated her employment. Annie was dismissed from her previous job due to an extraordinary once-in-a-lifetime circumstance.

After her new job interview, the new employer asked Annie's former employer for a reference. The former employer stated that Annie was an outstanding assistant but "rules are rules."

Annie has been at her current job as a valued team member for over seventeen years. Annie is a Registered Dental Assistant and has actively served 32 years total in the dental profession. She is on the board of a local Junior College Dental Assisting Program. She is presently an out-standing assistant, clinically skilled, and a great team member in the dental office where she works. Her current employer is happy and grateful to have found an outstanding new hire and to have her on board.

ACTION:

Reasonable adaptability to personal requests can provide a great opportunity for your office to acquire new talent. Rigid offices lose talented employees. Great HR managers are flexible. They are willing to individualize for talented team members, one employee at a time, and one day at a time.

There are many benefits to being considerate when it comes to personal time off. Your office will become a more desirable place to work. Individuals will suffer less from physical and psychological burnout. Workers may be healthier and happier. HR costs will be lower. It is not worth losing an outstanding and valuable team member over a once-in-a-lifetime request for personal leave.

HR managers who are inflexible often lose talented people. Beware of unsympathetic HR managers. Often these are people who themselves may have strained relationships with a spouse, children, close relatives, or business partners. Special arrangements for employees are few and far between. If someone has been a loyal and dedicated team member for many years, occasionally they may deserve a special pass.

Another example of a potentially good hire would be someone who has newly moved to your area. If you receive a resume or job inquiry from someone with experience and skill, a great attitude and previous loyal service at their former dental office, keep their resume on file until you have a job opening. Then invite them for an interview.

CASE STUDY 2: "THE NEW MOVE"

Marie and her family had just bought their first home. She was a new move to the area and her commute to her former dental office was a long distance. She had no orthodontic experience but she had a positive attitude and presented herself well. Her previous office gave her a glowing reference which stated that they were sad to lose her. She was seeking a new job closer to home. Marie had been with her previous dental office for fourteen years.

Marie was offered the job by unanimous decision. She quickly learned all the orthodontic skills and has been at her new office now for over sixteen years. Besides all of her clinical skills, she mastered HRM and became HR Coordinator for the office. She also became a Fellow of the American Association of Dental Office Managers and serves as office manager. Thorough and extremely well liked by her peers, Marie continues to be dedicated and makes sound judgments in the best interests of the patients and the practice. She is a trusted and valued team member.

ACTION:
Whenever you recruit or receive an excellent new resume, take the time to check references. The most important thing in the hiring process is good feedback from a reliable source and an honest resume with solid work history. There are also great benefits to involving the entire office in the hiring process. Team members will be working with the new recruit and can identify important characteristics needed for the job to be filled and whether the candidate has them. The candidate also needs to meet everyone in the work environment to make a sound judgment about whether your dental office is the place they want to work and where they will be happy. Bottom line, when you find someone great who just happened to move to your area, hire them or keep their resume on file until you can.

Chapter 2

ATTITUDE

Great attitude behaviors should be—
at a bare minimum—
treated as one among many
very important basic performance requirements.
– Bruce Tulgan

When it comes to recruitment of a new person for your dental office, we have a saying, "Attitude is everything." You will never go wrong if you hire someone based on an outstanding attitude and a desire to serve others. Skills can be taught. A positive attitude is a gift to the patients and the entire dental team.

Bruce Tulgan, in his book *The 27 Challenges Managers Face,* writes of the importance of "zeroing in on specific communication practices to drive great attitude behaviors." When you are surrounded by positive, happy people, you yourself become positive and happy, and this attitude is reflected to your dental patients and translates into their office experience and personal happiness.

A positive attitude of optimism is the most important new team-member attribute. To monitor the level of positive attitude within your dental team, I suggest an annual attitude test. The book *Little Gold Book of YES!* by Jeffrey Gitomer contains one such test. This test will reveal to each person their own area of attitude weakness. It reviews topics not to discuss, which bring down morale. Such topics include politics and the news. Negative events in the news are not to be discussed by team members in front of patients. If you find this happening in your dental office, one trick you could apply is to change the conversation by asking, "Isn't it a beautiful day?"

A positive attitude of optimism will also serve the office well in the persistence of pursuing office goals despite obstacles and minor setbacks. A positive attitude is also an emotional tendency that improves motivation, not only for the individual but also for everyone who works with them. Lastly, being around someone with a great positive attitude will continue to make the office a fun place to work. Positive attitudes are essential in the dental office.

Just like Disneyland, your dental office can strive to be the happiest place on earth. Positive attitudes will get you there. For the best customer service possible, consider dental patients as welcomed guests in your home. Think always of providing your patients with the best patient experience possible. As they say at Walt Disney World, "It's Showtime!"

How do you quickly assess and select a new team member for a positive attitude? You can start by evaluating the smile on the candidate's face. Smiling is a good sign of a positive attitude. What a blessing to be surrounded by a dental team of smiling, positive people.

CASE STUDY 3: "The Killer App"

Stasia first came to the dental office seeking an internship as a high school student. She had straight A's and a professional demeanor. She was constantly smiling and radiated beauty both inside and out. She lived at home with her parents and had a steady boyfriend. After high school graduation, she was seeking employment while she attended junior college to fulfill her requirements to become a hygienist.

Stasia completed the non-paid high school internship program. After high school, she was hired part-time at her request. The job was customized for her to meet her junior college school schedule. Her first assignment was check writing and bookkeeping. She completed this meticulously. When a full-time experienced team member resigned and Stasia had completed her junior college program, the doctor offered Stasia the full-time job.

The departing senior team member expressed hesitation in having young Stasia fulfill her former job duties as patient coordinator at the front desk. During training, the departing team member did not do much to help Stasia or to build her confidence. Stasia became nervous. She started to cry her first day on the job alone, thinking about all of her new responsibilities. The HR manager told Stasia, "I believe in you." She reminded Stasia that she was capable and that she had performed exquisitely over the past three years in the office. The doctor expressed that he had complete confidence in Stasia and in her ability at the front desk.

Over the next five years, Stasia mastered her new job. She fulfilled all front-desk duties and customer service with mastery. After many excellent and productive years, Staisa left to pursue her dream of further education and career development to become a dental hygienist. Staisia was capable at everything she had attempted. She was a talented and productive Gen Y'er. She was a "Killer App."

ACTION:

Where do you find promising and talented applicants who are fresh out of school? Seek referrals from counselors, teachers, even parents and patients in your practice. Sometimes even older experienced team members can refer friends, neighbors, or their own children.

When resumes reveal a track record of success, don't be afraid to promote young talent into senior positions of responsibility within your dental practice. Successful people committed to excellence tend to be dedicated to all that they do.

Chapter 3

THE THIRTEEN-STEP HIRING PROCESS

*Time spent on hiring
is time well spent.*
– Robert Half

The Thirteen-Step Hiring Process:

1. Resumes
2. Initial Phone Call
3. Checking References and Background Check
4. Office Meet and Greet
5. The Interview
6. License
7. Skills Assessment #1
8. Lunch
9. Team Meeting
10. Skills Assessment #2
11. The Unanimous Decision
12. Final Background Check
13. The Offer

S elect, don't hire. Take the time necessary to get to know the person to whom you are about to make a long-term commitment because you may be spending 40 hours a week for the next 20 years together. Give the hiring process the time and attention it needs and deserves. This is one of the most important types of decisions you will ever make in your dental office.

1. RESUMES

Request candidate CVs by email. If nothing else, this ensures that the candidate is up to date with computer use and able to use technology. You may want to post a reference number and ask candidates to quote that reference number in their cover letter. This is an easy way to screen out some people who don't read instructions or pay attention to detail.

Avoid wasting time with unnecessary walk-ins to your dental office. Do not include your address and phone number on your initial job-opening announcement. You may even want to set up a separate email address different from that of your office just to keep the hiring process organized and anonymous. Staying anonymous will minimize your practice disruption. Simply include an email address and fax number.

In this new economy, available candidates are plentiful, at least in California. I recall the experience of a podiatrist in San Francisco. Looking for a new office manager, she placed an ad on Craigslist. She received 500 resumes within one hour! Imagine if she had included the address and phone number on her announcement. She could have had 500 walk-ins! Her office would have been in total chaos.

Give every resume at least a glance. Good resumes show attention to detail. Spelling and accuracy are important.

Applicant history stated on the resume reveals many things. Great grades, for instance, demonstrate focus, concentration, and dedication. A good GPA could be one of many indicators that this person will be capable of being an outstanding addition to the office in the performance side of their tasks. A history of perfect attendance reveals responsibility and commitment. Combine this with a favorable behavioral interview, excellent attitude and great personality, and you may have a dental-team all-star.

Should the candidate's address be *voluntarily given,* close proximity to the office can be a key to long-term success. *You may not legally ask the candidate for their address during the hiring process.* We have found that for long-term tenure, individuals who live within a shorter driving distance tend to more readily stay at our place of employment. They are already dedicated members of our community. Your patients will also enjoy talking to and appreciate a local community member.

Employment history will reveal how many jobs the candidate has had and what types of jobs they have done. Since dentistry is a service industry, previous experience dealing with people and a focus on customer service is always a plus. Look for gaps in employment history as well. A stay of three or more years in one place is favorable. Employment change in less than one year more than twice could be a warning sign that this candidate may not be committed to their choice of work, or that they have a work-integration problem. A resume which displays constant job changes could be a sign that this applicant has performance or behavioral issues.

2. THE INITIAL PHONE CALL

Narrow your search to a reasonable number of candidates from all the resumes received. Ten is an ample number. Place an initial phone call to each applicant. Tell them about the job opening and ask a few questions. Have your questions prepared and ask the same questions of each candidate:

1. How did you hear about us?
2. What made you interested in working with us?
3. What can you tell me about what you do?
4. What can you tell me about our office?
5. When are you available for an interview if we choose you?
6. Does our pay scale work for you?
7. Do you have any questions for us?

Listen to how each person answers. Do you like the tone of their voice? Do they speak clearly? Are they polite? Are they enthusiastic? Do they sound energetic? Do you like what they have to say? How do you perceive their motivation for the job over the phone? Score the candidates on a scale of 1 to 10. Narrow your candidate pool down to the top five from the initial phone interview process.

3. CHECKING REFERENCES AND BACKGROUND CHECK

Always check references. You are looking for the statement that *the former employer would rehire.* Look at the source of the reference. Former employers rank highest. Former teachers or other references may or may not be reliable. You are looking to eliminate bad hires with no references, poor or negative references, and especially those with false references.

Find and verify the current employer or immediate past employer's telephone number by doing an independent search online. Check that the telephone number matches that given to you on the resume. Next, confirm that ***exact*** employment dates are the same ***exact*** dates given on the resume. Look for missing periods of time. Fudging employment dates is a good way to make unfavorable work history disappear and should be treated as an immediate red flag.

Reference check questions may include:

1. **"Would you rehire this person?"**
2. "What is your relationship to this person?"
3. "How long have you known this person?"
4. "Is there a reason to check public records?"
5. "Could you verify by fax or email the ***exact*** dates of employment?"
6. "Who was the employer prior to your employment?"
7. "Who was the employer after your employment?"
8. "What was their job title in your office?"
9. "What was your office pay rate?"

Asking the reference "How do you know this person?" and "How long have you known this person?" are important questions. Candidates may list a relative, co-worker, or friend rather than a previous employer as a reference. Check that the reference phone number is an actual place of employment by your online search. If the former employment was with another dental office, speak to the practice owner only. If the candidate says that they worked for Dr. Smith, call Dr. Smith, regardless of who they may have listed on the resume. If you are investigating non-dental employment, ask to speak to the HR director of the company from the online phone number to ensure employment.

When analyzing resumes, it helps to be a detective. Read between the lines. Investigate all claims related to job performance. Go online and *check for active licenses.* Be cautiously aware that information gathered online can contain things that an interviewer should not know. This information could be illegal to the interview process if it contains age, credit history, disabilities, religion or race not given on the resume. Once learned, this information cannot be unlearned. Furthermore, if gathered by an assistant, now there is a second party or witness to illegal acquisition. Stay within the boundaries of the job-performance interview process.

Should the candidate not fully disclose the truth, or if there are inconsistencies between the information you get from an applicant on the resume and what your background reference check uncovers, this is a big red flag. It is a definite NO. Should all inquiries come back positive, it is so far a YES.

When I'm hiring someone
I look for magic and a spark,
little things that intuitively give me a gut feeling
that this person will go to the ends of the earth
to accomplish the task at hand.
– Tommy Mottola

4. OFFICE MEET AND GREET
First impression

After checking references, further narrow your candidate pool to perhaps three. Schedule a fifteen-minute Meet and Greet, an initial in-person interview. Let each candidate know that this initial interview is typically 15 minutes but may run longer.

First impressions may present errors. It is important to do the steps of the office Meet and Greet before making a final decision. In the *Halo Effect*, our first impression may be very positive and concentrate only on the positive characteristics, which make us ignore the negative characteristics in the person. If the meeting starts with a very positive statement from the interviewee, this is often the case. In the *Horn Effect*, our first impression may be negative, leading us to ignore the positive characteristics of the candidate. If an interview starts with a negative statement, there is a higher chance that this may happen.

Give the office tour. Introduce the candidate to the team. After the full fifteen-minute minimum Meet and Greet ask yourself:

1. Do I like this person?
2. Are they smiling?
3. Are they pleasant?
4. Do they have a positive attitude?
5. Are they enthusiastic?
6. Do they give me a sense of peace and confidence in their abilities?
7. Will I be happy spending 8 hours a day, 5 days per week, with this person for the next 20 years?

Record your first impression, your "gut" feeling. Ask yourself "How will patients perceive the candidate? Do they make a good first impression?" If the answer to these questions is yes, continue the interview process.

Employment Application

At this initial visit, have a handwritten employment application for the candidate to fill out. Assess his or her handwriting. Once hired, the candidate's handwriting is something that you will need to read. Make sure writing is legible and that grammar, spelling, and punctuation are at the level of your office standards. Where results are positive, proceed forward with the short interview process.

Short interview

During the short interview, sit squarely across from the candidate and look them in the eyes. Do they look back at you in the eye? Looking away can be a sign of dishonesty. Give the candidate an overview of the job and the job duties. Don't sugarcoat the position. Ask them questions about their qualifications and talents for the job.

Previous pay rate is also a question that should be on your employment application. This figure can be checked before the initial interview. The figure of former pay can also be easily checked with the previous employer via fax or email verification. You may want to check that the pay rate listed is in the general range of what you are offering to pay. If not, you may need to give the candidate a general idea of what your job pay rate would be.

If you feel that all is positive and that the candidate is someone you may like to hire, ask them if they are interested in your job and whether they would like to proceed to a longer interview process or a working interview.

The older I get the less I listen to what people say
and the more I look at what they do.
– Andrew Carnegie

CASE STUDY 4: "THE TALKER"

Diane was interviewed as a candidate who had an excellent resume. She had ten years of experience in a well-known, well-respected dental office. She was articulate and enthusiastic over the phone. Then came the Meet and Greet interview.

Diane was an attractive woman, happy, friendly, and talkative … very, very, VERY talkative. She talked, and talked and TALKED. She was talkative to the point that there was not a moment of silence. Her voice was loud and extremely animated, paired with many wild arm gestures. She was packed with energy and constantly on the move.

Diane received the office tour. She played the video games. She met everyone on the team with excitement and shook their hands firmly with large up-and-down arm gestures. During the personal interview with the doctor, Diane gave many suggestions for what she saw as office improvements for this new office. She also guaranteed a 100% new-patient exam conversion rate.

When the Meet and Greet ended and Diane had gone, the doctor and team gathered to stare at each other in silence. Most were exhausted. Several had headaches. There was no need to discuss what had just happened. Someone finally broke the silence by saying, "I need a tranquilizer!"

ACTION:
When evaluating the candidate at the Meet and Greet, confirm your first impression with reference checks. Be consistent with your questions at each step of the interview process so that candidates are treated fairly. At any point where you feel that the candidate is not a fit for your job opening or that they do not meet your job requirements, move on.

There are a few warning signs to look for during the initial interview:

1. Loud and disruptive behavior
2. Fidgeting, stiffness, or no mirroring of body language
3. Grimaces and smirks
4. Lack of eye contact

5. Poor posture
6. Folded arms or lack of hand movement

Ask yourself: "What is my gut feeling regarding this candidate?" *Your initial gut-feeling instinct is critical.* Life experiences add up, are remembered, and triggered by your mind into a tightening of your body. Your gut is saying to you "this doesn't feel right." Listen to it. It's a *kinesthetic* feel some people have as a strong intuition. It is mind and body wisdom. To ignore it is to ignore life's wisdom at your own peril.

If someone "rubs you the wrong way," it is likely that they will rub patients the wrong way as well, and annoy the dentist and team members, too. Don't be afraid to be honest with yourself about your true feelings. Initial concerns about the candidate are very important and cause you to doubt if you made the right decision. It is possible that the behavior you are initially concerned about will only get worse.

5. THE INTERVIEW

If the candidate has successfully passed the initial short interview and you would like to learn more, schedule a formal long interview. Give the process adequate time, thirty minutes to an hour, and your undivided attention. You may want two people, perhaps the doctor and the HR or office manager, to both separately interview the candidate. Interviews can follow the Meet and Greet or be rescheduled for another time.

For time and efficiency, have standard questions prepared ahead of time. This will also be helpful in having consistency of evaluation and comparison between candidates.

An important interview question is "Why did you leave your last job?" Most candidates are looking for a better opportunity or more money. Often though, they leave because they may have found their previous employer to be too demanding. Or, perhaps the employee didn't get along with the boss or other teammates. If you sense this is the situation, probe deeper to get a clearer picture of the suitability of the candidate.

One question you may not ask is "How many days were you absent last year?" This question is not legal under the Americans with Disabilities Act. For more information on illegal interview questions, see your own state guidelines. In California, see the California Department of Fair Employment and Housing *Pre-Employment Inquiry Guidelines* at www.dfeh.ca.gov.

In an effort to follow the law, here are some unlawful questions you should never ask and acceptable, legal alternative interview questions.

Illegal and Acceptable Interview Questions

As a general rule: if the question isn't related directly to the performance of the job, don't ask it. Not only could this type of personal question not be legal, it could also adversely influence your decision to hire a good person for the job.

In the state of California, there are several questions that you are not allowed to ask. Stated here are some questions you should never ask and their counterpart of acceptable verbiage.

Name

The law prohibits making employment decisions based on gender stereotypes. Inquiries about name may be viewed as discriminatory, especially a name that would indicate ancestry or national origin. Marital status or other domestic partnership may not be questioned.

Illegal

"State your *maiden* name."

"Do you prefer to be called Mr., Mrs., Miss or Ms.?

"Have you ever used another name?"

Acceptable

"State your name"

"Is there any additional information regarding your name, use of an assumed name, nickname, or any other name which would enable us to check your work records?"

Gender

It is important not to make assumptions about a person's abilities based on their gender.

Illegal

"We've always had a man in this job. Do you think you, as a female, can handle it?"

Acceptable
"What do you have to offer our company?"
"Tell me about your experience managing teams."
"Have you ever been disciplined for your behavior at work?"

Marital and Family Status

A candidate may *volunteer* "I have young children and can't work past 4:39 p.m." If the job requires evening work, such a restriction would make the candidate not a fit for the job. Beware not to ask personal marital and family questions.

Illegal
"When are you planning to have children?"
"If you get pregnant, will you continue to work?"
"Who will take care of your children while you're at work?"
"Can you get a babysitter on short notice?"
"What do your parents do for a living?"

Acceptable
"Are you able to start work at 8:00 a.m.?"
"What hours can you work?"
"Are you available to work overtime?"
"How did you become interested in dentistry?"
"What are your long-term career goals?"
"This practice treats a lot of children. What is your experience working with children?"

Notice in Case of Emergency

Beware not to use this question to inquire about marital status or children.

Illegal
"Who is your closest relative to notify in case of emergency?"

Acceptable
Once hired, it is acceptable to ask, "Please list the name and address of the person to be notified in case of an emergency."

Residence

Since your home could be an indication of your financial status or connected to neighborhood discrimination, it is not legal to ask about it.

Illegal
"Do you own or rent your home?"
"Do you live nearby?"
"How far is your commute?"
"Did you ever live in a foreign country?"

Acceptable
"How long have you lived at your current residence?"
"How long did you live at your past residence?"
"Are you willing to relocate?"
"What is the best phone number for us to reach you?"

Age

It's important that you don't make assumptions about a candidate's maturity based on age. Federal child-labor laws state that the minimum age to work is 14 (with some exceptions). In the state of California, a child employment certificate is needed for children under the age of 18 while enrolled in school. This certificate is provided by the labor department in your state or may be provided by the school. When there is a conflict between federal and state laws regarding child labor age, the more restrictive law will apply.

Illegal
"State your birthdate."
"State your age."
"How old are you?"
"What year did you graduate from high school?"
"Are you over the age of 40?"
"How much longer do you plan to work before your retire?"

Acceptable
"Will you be able to verify that you meet the legal age requirement for the job?"
"Are you over the age of 18?"

"What are your long-term career goals?"

Nationality

It is not acceptable to ask questions regarding the citizenship of parents, spouse, or other relatives. It is also not even acceptable to ask the candidate for the date when citizenship was acquired. Any questions about the gathering or production of any papers or documentation of naturalization *prior to hire* are off limits, at least in the state of California.

Illegal

"Where was your birthplace?"

"Where were your parents' birthplaces?"

"Where was your spouse's birthplace?"

"Where were your children's birthplaces?"

"Are you a U.S. citizen?"

"What is your native tongue?"

Acceptable

"What languages do you speak?"

"Are you authorized to work and remain in the United States?"

"Can you, after employment, submit verification of your legal right to work in the United States?"

Physical Condition, Handicap, or Disability

It is not legal to question the applicant's weight, height, general health, medical conditions or illnesses. It is also not legal to question whether the applicant has ever received workers' compensation benefits. Questions about a candidate's physical characteristics are prohibited, as are questions about a person's actual disability.

Candidates can be given a job description of the physical requirements of the job. Then questions about their ability to fulfill the job can be asked.

Illegal

"How did you get that physical abnormality or disability?"

"Do you have any physical conditions or handicaps?"

"Do you have now, or have you ever had, a drug or alcohol problem?"

"Have you ever been out on disability or filed a disability claim against a previous employer?"

"How tall are you?"

"How much do you weigh?"

"Have you had any illnesses or operations?"

Acceptable

Once the person has received a job description you may ask,

"Are you able to perform the duties of the position for which you have applied, with or without an accommodation?"

"This is a drug-free work place. Are you taking any drugs which may affect your job?"

"Do you have any issues with any task of the job including wearing gloves?"

Military Service

It is unacceptable to ask general questions regarding military service, such as dates and type of discharge. The interviewer cannot ask questions about the effect of the candidate's military service on his ability of work for the employer.

Illegal

"Did you ever serve in the U.S. military?"

"Did you ever serve in a foreign military?"

"Are you a member of the National Guard or Reserves?"

"How often are you deployed for your Army Reserve training exercises?"

"Were you honorably discharged from the military?"

Acceptable

"What skills did you acquire regarding this job and where did you learn them?"

"Do you have any upcoming events that would require time away from work?"

Arrest, Criminal Record

The U.S. Equal Employment Opportunity Commission (EEOC) cautions that many cases may have been dismissed without a conviction. San Francisco's Fair Chance Ordinance (FCO) goes so far as to direct that employers within their municipality may not inquire on the job application the fact or detailing of any conviction history or unresolved arrests or any criminal record topics that are off-limits at any time. Only after a conditional offer of employment can inquire be made about "conviction history" or "unresolved arrests." Be sure to act in keeping with federal, state, county, and municipal directives.

Illegal
  "Have you ever been arrested?"

Acceptable
  "Have you ever been convicted of a felony, fraud, or theft?"
  Such a question must be accompanied by a statement that a conviction will not necessarily disqualify an applicant from employment in the State of California.

Organizations, Activities

Many organizations may be religious, ethnic, or of marital status in nature. You therefore may not ask about them, as the response could lead to discrimination.

Illegal
  "List all organizations, clubs, societies, and social organizations to which you belong."

Acceptable
  "Please list job-related organizations, clubs, professional societies or trade groups that are relevant to our industry. You may omit those which indicate your race, religious creed, color, national origin, ancestry, sex, or age."

Religion

Protect yourself from overstepping the boundaries of religion during the interview process.

Illegal
  "What religion do you practice?"
  "What religious holidays do you observe?"

Acceptable

Once the candidate has received a copy of the office schedule, you may ask, "Can you work the schedule required of this job?"

Most states will have protections in place for religious accommodations which will need to be followed.

Personal Finances

Illegal

"Do you own a car?"

"Do you own a home?"

"Are your wages garnished?"

"Have you ever declared personal bankruptcy?"

Acceptable

"Will you be able to arrive at work 15 minutes prior to the start of the workday?"

Education

Asking for dates of education could lead to age discrimination. Be sure not to ask questions related to dates of graduation.

Illegal

"When was the date when you completed high school?"

Acceptable

"Which school did you attend?"

"What professional education prepares you for this job?"

References

When asking about references, stay away from questions which may elicit a response regarding race, religion, national origin, ancestry, physical handicap, medical condition, marital status, age, sex, gender preference, or any other protected classification.

Illegal

"Did someone from your church refer you here?"

Acceptable

"Why did you leave your last job?"

"By whom were you referred for a position here?"

"Please list the name of a person willing to provide a professional reference."

6. Current License

Licenses can be checked online. The only proper verification of licensure is to confirm directly with the issuing authority. Don't take the candidate's word that his or her license is current without seeing the documentation. Ask to have a copy of the current license sent and wait to receive it.

When not current, candidates often say that their licenses will arrive by a certain date. Through experience, I have found that this usually is not the case. Hiring someone with the promise of a current license is risky. It may be that part of the state board was not passed, and, in some cases, it may never be passed. Worse, there could be legal matters preventing the candidate from ever getting their licenses.

Asking for the current license also applies to hiring a dental associate. Licenses may be checked online and printed from the dental board website. Check the state license listing from where the dentist or dental assistant may have moved. It is possible that a license may have been lost in another state. Should a license not be forthcoming, you may want to investigate further.

CASE STUDY 5: "The Accomplice"

Delores had been a dental office intern. As an older student, she graduated from her dental assisting program with flying colors. But her license was delayed. The delay lasted years. Everyone in the office could not figure out what was taking Delores's license so long to arrive. Then came the truth. In her younger years, Delores had made a bad choice in a boyfriend.

Due to her boyfriend's influence during her teen years, Delores had been arrested with drugs in her car. She claimed the drugs were her boyfriend's. It didn't matter. They were in her car and she made the choice to have this boyfriend. Her boyfriend had also gotten her in trouble with the law. This bad decision and association early in life prevented Delores from ever becoming a registered dental-assistant licensed in the state of California. Even Delores didn't know during her RDA schooling process that she would never be eligible for licensure.

ACTION:

Require a physical license or verify licenses on the state dental-assisting website prior to job offer and employment. Don't take someone's word that they have a license or that their license is pending and will arrive soon. If there is a delay in dental licensure, check it out immediately. Ask to see the physical license prior to giving a hire offer. Check out the reason for licensure delay with the dental board. You may need to access other public records.

7. SKILLS ASSESSMENT #1

Once the verbal review process is successfully passed, invite the potential new hire for a skills assessment. Evaluate the individual's ability to complete the tasks to be performed. This day will give you valuable information about the person's future potential and ability to learn on the job.

Assess how eager the interviewee is to jump in and participate. Is she genuinely motivated and interested in the patients and the work, or is she standing by like a wallflower?

Discern what you can during this day about work ethic, attitude, and common sense. I like to give a simple, straightforward test: "the Cotton Roll Test." I purposely drop a cotton roll onto the floor. This can also be done with a dental instrument. Will the person I am considering as a new assistant have the common sense to pick it up on her own and place it to the side in the sterilization area? Must they be told to pick up the cotton roll or the dental instrument and that it is now unsterile? If they have to be told, I consider this a very poor omen of future work potential. This may seem like a ridiculous test. I assure you, it is not.

At the initial interview, you need to discern the candidate's common sense in being able to evaluate a situation, decide on their own what needs to be done, and jumping in to help out the patient and improvement of the office. This is work ethic and service in action. These are desirable workplace behaviors. These are what you want in a new hire and what you need to have in order for your dental office run smoothly.

Should you want to test manual skills, it is best to do so on a typodont rather than a live patient. Skills assessment is important. Pre-test for as many important skills for the job as you possibly can.

You need a collaborative hiring process.
– Steve Jobs

8. LUNCH

During the employment screening process, have your assistants take the person being interviewed out to lunch without the doctor. This will give your team time to talk casually to get a feel for this new person. People being interviewed may behave differently when the doctor is not around. Without the doctor, they will feel and act more relaxed. It is important for the team to determine whether or not the candidate will be a good fit, a sense of someone they can work with well.

A team lunch will also give everyone the opportunity to ask questions that they may not feel comfortable asking in the presence of the doctor. At this time, the team also has the opportunity to say nice things about the doctor, their team, and the office work environment in which they work to encourage the candidate to accept the job offered should they receive it. This candidate lunch is a job function for which team members will need to be paid. (Please note that in California, after this lunch and five hours of work, a half-hour break must still be given before returning to work.) Plan your interview lunch carefully. It will give you valuable information and may help you to make your final decision.

9. TEAM MEETING

After the Skills Assessment #1, poll everyone in your office to decide whether to pursue the present person further or to keep looking. At this point, maybe you will narrow the interview process down to only two people. Invite these two back for Skills Assessment #2.

10. SKILLS ASSESSMENT #2

At this interview, let the assistant perform the job that they will actually be doing in the office. Let the applicant answer the phone or simulate a patient procedure on a typodont. Monitor the skill as it is being done. Be aware that although this individual has not been hired, they are your employee during the interview process if they are doing real work in the office. It is best to have a clinical simulation on a typodont and have the interviewee be unpaid.

Imagine that this person has filled the position and that he or she is performing their new job in your office. Are you happy with their performance? Are you and the entire workforce comfortable with the candidate? Is she open to your suggestions of how you would like things done in your office?

Sometimes you will hear, "In my previous office, we didn't do it this way." This is the response of a candidate who is *NOT* highly trainable. Be cautious if you already hear this type of response.

Ask yourself, "Does this candidate interact well with the other team members? Do you hear positive responses? Does the candidate appear to enjoy serving your patients and do they appear to be enjoying her?"

Someone could be amazing at what they do,
but if you don't like them, why bother hiring them?
– Chip Conley

11. THE UNANIMOUS DECISION
There may be an individual who is not in favor of hiring the candidate. Everyone carries their own outlook, attitude and personality. What if the decision isn't unanimous? Take the discussion seriously. The dental office has a small workforce that will need to perform closely together in harmony. Work towards finding a candidate who can be hired without objection.

When the new member is hired by unanimous decision, the full team is devoted to making this new person a success in the dental office. Everyone will be working together to help her achieve a high level of performance. In this situation, people will agree that the decision to hire her was a good decision. Now it's time to make it work.

12. FINAL BACKGROUND CHECK
The final background check is separate from a previous employer verification. It is a well-planned background check with an outside agency. It may include a criminal records check, public records check, credit history check, drug test, social security number scan, employment verifications and education verifications, DMV records, or "digital dirt."

It is not illegal for an employer to ask questions about an applicant's or employee's background, or to require a background check. We must be very careful what we ask for to be in line with federal and state laws that protect applicants and employees from discrimination. These laws are enforced by the Equal Employment Opportunity Commissions (EEOC). In addition, dental practice owners must comply with the Fair Credit Reporting Act (FCRA) enforced by the Federal Trade Commission (FTC).

Seek a professional to help you to understand your obligations before, during, and after the background check. Make a background check standard for all new employees, to treat everyone equally. *The employee should never be allowed to work, see a patient, or have access to any private health information or credit card information until after passing the background check.*

There are federal and state background check rules. You will need to acquire a written release for an extensive background check. The FCRA requires that you *get permission in writing* beforehand and make known the following:

1. That you may use the information to make the decision about their employment.
2. It is their right to a description of the scope of the investigation.
3. That you have their written permission to do the background check.
4. Certification to the company doing the report that you notified the applicant and complied with FCRA requirements to not discriminate against the applicant or misuse the information in violation of federal or state equal opportunity laws or regulations.

In California, there is the "California 7-Year Rule" which restricts how far back an employer can go when conducting employment background checks. This would protect someone busted for marijuana in seventh grade. Sadly, 65 million Americans have a criminal record and over 70% of resumes contain at least some false or misleading information. It is possible that even the last employer may not be aware of information which may come to light in a background check.

In California as of January 2012, California law restricts employers from use of credit reports even for those who will be handling collections in your dental office. California also restricts use of California Workers' Compensation Form discussion or investigation. To find out more about federal laws relating to background reports in your state, visit www.business.ftc.gov.

13. The Job Offer

Have the doctor and/or HR Director tell the final applicant about the position. Don't sugarcoat the job description or its duties. Outline the challenges. Ask the candidate what difficulties she faced on her last job and how she feels this job would compare. Ask her if she feels this is a position she would like and one that she could handle and a good fit for her talents.

Remember, a dental office is a desirable place to work. Scale of compensation should be based upon the candidate's qualifications. The Ritz Carlton pays the same as other hotels in their industry. Have an employment agreement written in terms which are understood easily and that includes pay rate. Ask the candidate to sign the terms offered, as outlined in your job offer in writing, should he or she accept the job at this time.

Choose the best person at the price you are willing to pay. Present your desired rate, range and benefits. Ask if the dollar amount and benefits package is acceptable. Make your offer. *Be cautious of what you put into writing.* Employers often create inadvertent contracts by what they put into writing. It can end up costing them thousands of dollars if things don't work out.

Now it is the moment of truth: the final candidate either accepts your job offer or does not accept it. If the answer is "NO," try again. If the answer is "YES," congratulations, a successful journey has brought you together. Shake hands and celebrate.

Part Two

INTEGRATION

In any collaboration,
assistants are as valuable as you allow them to be.
Treat assistants with respect and you will gain
valuable collaborators.
– Twyla Tharp

Welcome to the team! We are now ready to start to integrate the new hire into our office culture. Quickly, you must build in the new employee the vision, mission, and shared core values of your dental office to make them a stakeholder and collaborator in success. This process will take communication, integration, motivation, and collaboration.

On the very first day, take time to review expectations, management systems, and rules and regulations of the office with the new hire. Answer all questions. Communicate openly and frequently from then on. This will make the integration process smooth for you, the team, and the new hire.

Try the rule of a cheerful "Good Morning" and a "Fond Farewell." Each morning, look each other in the eye and give a pleasant hello; each evening before leaving the office, ask each person if they need any additional help before you give a fond farewell. This is a great way to start and end communication each day. It is our basic rule of teamwork, collaboration, and courtesy. It is also an assurance that everyone takes time to care about each other, help each other, support each other, and communicate openly. It is a guarantee that no one is left behind alone at the end of the day with the burden of uncompleted work.

The Morning Huddle

You may want to start your day with a morning huddle. This assures that everyone is there, focused, and ready to start the day. "What's in the show today?" You may want to have an agenda. Ideas may include:

1. Any special patient considerations for the day?
2. Any changes in the schedule for today?
3. Any emergencies today?
4. Are there any lunchtime meetings for the doctor?
5. Does anyone have any special considerations today?
6. Are there any special payments which need to be collected?
7. GO TEAM! "It's Showtime!"

Sports teams have an initial huddle but continue to huddle throughout the game. Target has their morning huddle a little later in the morning once the workday has started. You may choose to have your huddle at any time you wish. What's important is to start your day with communication, motivation, and enthusiasm and then maintain it throughout the day, until the very last patient is gone.

As the leader, if you clearly conveyed that teamwork and collaboration are expected and have that written down in the Team Handbook, you can reinforce policy by saying, "I made it clear to everyone that it's an office rule that we help each other before leaving for lunch and for the day. In this instance, you certainly did not follow our team rule of helping out. Please be sure not to let this happen again." You will be backed up by what is written in the Handbook as procedures and policies, to which the employee has signed in agreement. Reviewing the rules regularly will simplify your office life and set clear expectations for everyone. This will make it easier to deal with situations. Your HRM will run smoothly.

Chapter 4

THE TEAM HANDBOOK

*Working in a dental office without a handbook
is like living in a lawless land.*
– Ann Marie Gorczyca

C ountries have laws, dental offices have rules. No office is safe without a written procedures and policies manual, the employment
manual or *The Team Handbook*. It is a behavior guide making it easy for
team members to understand the standards, the mission, the core values,
and rules of their dental office in which they are employed. Team members must accept and abide by these office rules of conduct. This is not a
contract but a standard you set for those who work in your dental office.

If you want something understood and accepted, communicate
it. Your office members cannot read your mind. If you want important
office practices clearly understood and followed, write them in the Team
Handbook.

WRITTEN AFFIRMATION

Get off to a great start. Ask a new hire to *read the Team Handbook the
first day of work*. Tell her, "I am going to pay you for 1 hour to read the
Team Handbook. Once you have read it, sign that you have read it, have
asked questions, and understand its contents, I will pay you." It is best
to be absolutely sure that the new team member read the handbook

thoroughly and to have this documented. Have your new hire read the handbook on the clock and note that in her time records along with the written affirmation. This could prove useful in the future.

Receive a written affirmation that states that the new hire has read the Handbook and *is aware of all that is stated there.* Be sure to obtain a signed acknowledgement of receipt from each team member that they have read the most recent Handbook. Store these affirmations in each personnel file.

Employment At-Will

One very important function of the Team Handbook is to clearly state that the employment terms are "Employment At-Will." This policy will state that an employee is hired as at-will and either party, with or without cause, can terminate the employment relationship at any time. This termination may not violate any specific laws. "This At-Will agreement cannot be changed unless in writing agreed to by management." This policy gives the employer the right to terminate the employee when need be. All states, except Montana, recognize at-will employment. Benefits are also At-Will. Benefits can be changed. Management has the right to change benefits as finances permit.

Be careful of the language you use with employees regarding the Employment At-Will status. You may also want to place it on your job application. An employer may say things like "You'll always have a place here," or "As long as you do great work you will be able to stay here." When statements like this are made repeatedly, especially at a job interview or job offer, the employer may be violating the at-will employment law and limiting their ability to fire someone at will in the future.

In all scenarios, you will have written documentation of awareness of required policies and procedures as well as codes of conduct. This is important in all states and particularly in California, where the employer is far more likely to prevail during Unemployment Benefit hearings when written policies exist, are current, and have been acknowledged.

Your handbook is best created by an HR professional with legal experience who specializes in dental practices, and is well familiar with state and federal laws. Protect the office legally, should something go awry with all hires. Keep your Handbook current, and update every year as state and federal employment laws change.

What many of us don't know about HR and Employment Law and Handbooks can harm us. For example, although tempting, made-up policies such as "No gossiping" and "Everything in the office is confidential" may actually create a legal liability.

CASE STUDY 6: "THE ENFORCER"

Helen had been a manager at a leading national-chain drugstore. She had decided to make a career shift into dentistry. After completing her schooling, she completed her internship in the office and was excellent. When the time came, she was immediately hired as a registered dental assistant into the office where she interned. But there was one problem. This was a new office and did not have a policy and procedure Handbook.

With years of experience in HRM, Helen knew better than the doctor that this was a workplace hazard for both the doctor and the team. She told the doctor that she would not work in an office without a team Handbook. The doctor did not even know what a Team Handbook was at the time. Helen knew that without a Team Handbook, policies and procedures would not exist, be known, followed, or enforced. Work would be chaos. Although extreme, Helen quit. This was reason enough for her to leave. The doctor got a handbook immediately thereafter and updated it every year ever since.

ACTION:

This case study is a true story. It happened to me my first year in practice. I lost a fantastic team member for not having a Policy and Procedures Manual. This is perhaps why, in addition to the safety of having and implementing a Team Handbook, I emphasize the importance of having a handbook so much. Those with experience in HR management know that a Team Handbook or Policy and Procedures Manual is crucial for workplace order and fairness as well as adherence to employment law.

It would have been helpful if Helen had stayed through the process of construction of the customized Team Handbook by an HR professional and helped to integrate its use in the new office. Many dentists do not have this important policy and procedure manual in place the first day that they open their dental practice and already have their first hire. Although legally risky, initial lack of a handbook in a new office is common. Many consider it essential prior to their first day of employment. I agree wholeheartedly. I wish I had learned about the importance of a policy and procedure handbook in dental school or that it would have been emphasized during my residency program.

Later, I suffered again from not having a Team Handbook when I first felt the need to terminate one of my employees. A dental colleague whom I had asked for advice asked, "Did you have her sign the 90-day introductory "Employment At-Will" statement in the Team Handbook?" After asking, "What's that?" my answer was "No." I learned for the first time that a dismissed team member without a 90-day introductory period agreement would file for unemployment which could lead to an increased unemployment rate for the office to pay in the future. I never dismissed this team member for lack of this signed agreement. She carried on at a low level for a little bit longer and eventually quit.

Attorneys often state that it is difficult to defend dental clients on employment issues when there is no documentation of having a Team Handbook that is legal and up to date. When opening a new office, put creation and enforcement of a Team Handbook at the top of your list of dental office necessities.

The Team Handbook states that the employer reserves their Employment At-Will rights. The employer has this signed document of receipt to place into the personnel file of each employee on workday one. It documents the 90-day introductory period. It serves as documented explanation of the employer's right to terminate should this be necessary.

The Team Handbook can be amended year to year. As state employment laws change, it will need to be updated and reviewed with all team members, best on an annual basis. Newly signed acceptance of receipt will be placed in personnel files. Team members will sign an acknowledgement of any and all changes to the policies. Your Team Handbook can be locked up or stored in electronic format for easy access.

Once you have your Team Handbook, follow it regularly. Don't retreat, advance!

In the following pages are several topics contained in a typical Team Handbook, with explanation of the ways these rules are important and how they will help you with HRM. It is impossible here to describe in detail every single topic found in the Team Handbook. This topic is itself a book. Outlined are topics of a Team Handbook as they relate to the chapters of this book.

1. Introduction to the Organization. Employment "At Will."
2. Recruitment. Employment. Conflicts of Interest.
3. Integration. Employment Status and Records. Reviews.
4. Team Management. Work Conditions and Hours.
5. Team Management. Behaviors. Team Member Conduct.
6. Employment Law. Leaves of Absence.
7. Distribution of Resources. Benefits.
8. Distribution of Resources. Timekeeping and Payroll.

Chapter 5

THE 90-DAY INTRODUCTORY PERIOD

When I'm hiring a cook for one of my restaurants,
and I want to see what they can do,
I usually ask them to make me an omelet.
– Bobby Flay

Without doubt, the first 90-calendar-day Introductory Period is critical for setting work performance expectations. During this initial Introductory Period, the new hire has been given the office ground rules and lots of training and feedback. The Team Handbook has been reviewed and the written receipt of acceptance has been received by the HR manager and placed in the new hire's personnel file. It is up to the new hire to comply with the policies of the office as outlined in the Team Handbook. The new team member will receive coaching and one-on-one feedback during this Introductory Period to get off to a great start and smoothly integrate into the office.

The three-month Introductory Period is a make-or-break time for the new team member. Where allowed by law, the Introductory Period can be a buffer-zone time during which no benefits are accrued or earned. In this situation, the eligibility for other benefits do not start until this period, usually 90 calendar days, has been successfully completed.

Explain the alignment that is necessary for your new hire to fit your office culture, teamwork, and the quality of care that you deliver. Since it is easiest to dismiss the new hire during this time with minimal unemployment responsibilities, it is important that you use this period wisely. Do not overlook or make excuses for undesirable actions and disappointing performance during the first 90 days. This is the time when new team members should be on their best behavior. Think of it as the "honeymoon" period. Undesirable, annoying, and unacceptable behaviors during this Introductory Period in most cases will only get worse with time. Cut your losses early and move on if need be. On the contrary, if all is well during the Introductory Period, celebrate! You have a keeper!

During the 90-day Introductory Period, the new hire merges with an existing office culture. This is not easy. The new hire will be shown systems new to them, be coached, given feedback and guidance, and ultimately tested to ensure that they are a good fit. "That's not how I do it," could mean one of two things: the new hire has a new better system or they are not coachable. This is for you to decide, quickly.

The new team member is also testing her new office environment as well. If it is not a fit for either of you, it is possible that the new hire will voluntarily quit within the first month. Whatever expectations you have for this new addition, they need to be met during the first 90-day Introductory Period.

Be honest with yourself and your team about your true feelings regarding a new hire. Ask all present in the office for feedback. If performance is not great during the initial 90-day period, it may not improve. Not everyone is teachable. If this is the case and there is questioning about the wisdom of the decision, cut your losses and try again.

Review performance daily starting with the first day. The first week will be the most difficult. Set up a buddy system and assign a senior team member to guide the new hire the first week. Once the new hire has caught on to office systems and performance has reached an acceptable level, continue to review performance weekly throughout the Introductory Period. Be as detailed and precise about expectations as possible. Suggestions for improvement may need to be repeated two or three times. This is a delicate time which sets the tone for the future.

As the new member becomes more familiar with her job duties, daily improvements, increased confidence, and independence should be seen. Where a new team member falls short, the doctor or HR managers need to communicate the issue that needs improvement immediately to the new hire. These conversations need to be documented.

HR specialist Paul Edwards of CEDR Solutions www.cedrsolutions. com recommends the following Introductory Period review meeting rules to remember:

1. Attack the problem in performance, not the person.
2. Communicate the impact of their poor performance on the practice.
3. Review previous discussions on the same matter.
4. Clearly state what the expected improvement and performance standard would be.
5. Document the conversation in writing.
6. *Always have the employee acknowledge the conversation of their desired corrective action in writing, with the date and employee's signature.*

The behavior of all those around the new hire also needs to adapt during this period of integration of a new team member. The addition of a new hire is an adjustment period for everyone in the office. Potential jealousies or feelings of turf infringement may develop. Be prepared for this. Deal with these issues quickly and openly for the benefit of the new addition and everyone on the team including the doctor, the office, and especially the patients.

Ask the new team member regularly "How is it going?" Ask others in the office the same question. Encourage the new hire to ask questions and state when something is unknown or difficult for them rather than continue ahead in uncertainty.

Assess teamwork. There may be tension associated with change. Teams test "the new kid on the block." They may initially feel frustrated with the extra work of training and integrating a new person. Sometimes there is jealousy about "the shiny new toy." There will be bumps in the road. Teamwork and the new team-member performance should improve each day and continue to move closer to ideal.

In the end, it's important to determine and evaluate if this new team member is workable and someone you desire as a permanent member of your team. The answer needs to be a certain and confident "Yes."

CASE STUDY 7: "THE CHOKER"

A receptionist's job was available in the dental office. Nellie had heard about the opening from one of her friends who was a present team member in the dental office. The present team member knew Nellie well and gave her a strong recommendation for the job.

Nellie had never worked in a dental office before. She knew nothing of dentistry and had never met the doctor before. She was an attractive woman who presented herself well. She gave the appearance that she would be capable of handling the job of dental receptionist.

She was interviewed and hired. Since the office was in immediate need of the new receptionist, they did not *"waste time"* evaluating Nellie's skill set as a receptionist or have her do any telephone-answering role-playing during the interview evaluation period.

Nellie was shown how to answer the phone on day one of her new job as receptionist. She was given a script, coaching, and time to practice. On the first day of the 90-day Introductory Period, Nellie now sat waiting and prepared for her turn to answer the phone.

Then the phone rang. The first time Nellie answered the phone, she did not pronounce the doctor's name correctly. Even though she had practiced, when the time came for action, she did not perform well. The phone rang again. The second time Nellie answered the phone she froze into a speechless stupor. This disappointing performance continued all day with every phone call. By the end of day one, the doctor and team determined that Nellie had not been capable of answering the phone well even once. She had choked every time.

The excuses flew right and left. Perhaps she was nervous? Perhaps she was overwhelmed? We all think that everyone deserves a second chance. Nellie was given honest feedback and coached. She was given a chance to improve. Improvement would be seen the next day if it were to be seen at all.

Feeling a bit sorry for Nellie, the doctor and team decided to invite Nellie back for working day two. On working day two, answering the phone was still a strain. The first call did not go well, nor the second, nor the third. At that point, the doctor pulled Nellie into the office and asked her if she felt that this position was not a match for her. Nellie admitted that she was finding the front desk position stressful and difficult.

There was no need to continue what was turning into a painful experience for all involved. The doctor assumed leadership and cut to the chase. In a pleasant one-on-one, Nellie was thanked for applying for the job but told that it was not a fit for her talents. She was told that today would be her last day in the office. Nellie was given a prepared check payment and thanked for her time.

Nellie became very angry. She stormed out of the office. Then she wrote the doctor a nasty letter delivered the next day. She claimed that she was not given a chance to perform her job function. The letter went into her 2-day personnel file with the documentation of the work quality which Nellie displayed during her two days as receptionist, with the descriptions of the poorly answered phone calls during the 90-day Introductory Period.

ACTION:

Testing skill sets and role-playing are extremely valuable during the time of the interview. Testing performance for the particular job duties needed saves time and money in the long run. Poor job performance during the 90-day Introductory Period can be prevented by skill testing and role-playing at the interview. Observe the actual task to be performed in the job in Skill Test #1 and confirm it in Skill Test #2 at the interview prior to hire. If performance during the interview process is poor, it is doubtful that there will be change for an individual to function well in this position no matter how many days they spend on the job.

Hiring friends of team members often creates an uneven playing field and clouds the decision-making process. When friends and family get involved in the decision-making process, you may find yourself hiring someone as a favor to a team member or friend rather than choosing the strongest candidate objectively for the job.

You may want to test other skill sets such as tray setup or sterilization functions. Hire when performance is good. When performance is poor, accept that some people are not suited for certain tasks and that not everyone is trainable. With more extensive interviewing and testing prior to hire, mismatched job situations and the need for dismissal of a new hire during the Introductory Period will be diminished.

Personnel file

During the 90-day Introductory Period, it is essential to make sure that the personnel file is complete. An employee may have access to his or her personnel file by giving advanced written notice. In either hard-copy or electronic form it will need the following documents:

1. Resume
2. Employment application
3. Hiring confirmation with "At-Will" language

Once you have your new hire, there are several documents on the HRM checklist that will need to be obtained as early as the first day of employment. These include:

4. Personal information sheet
5. Direct deposit pay form
6. Copies of all current licenses, CPR certification, and immunization documents
7. W-4 Federal and State (DE-4 in CA) employee's tax withholding allowance
8. I-9 Form, Employment Eligibility Verification
9. New hire reporting Form DE-34 Employment Development Department (EDD)
10. Initial safety training documentation
11. Signed copy of receipt of the Team Handbook
12. Sexual Harassment information sheet
13. Time of Hire Form 3551 Worker's Compensation information
14. DE 2515 State Disability Insurance Provisions (SDI) Brochure outlines DI program
15. Paid Family Leave (PFL) form
16. Health Insurance Portability and Accountability Act (HIPAA) form
17. Health insurance forms
18. Employee property return agreement
19. Acknowledgement of office key

There are numerous HR outsourcing companies from which dentists may choose to obtain these materials and further assistance. Use a company recommended by fellow dentists in your community. Some insurance companies such as The Dentist's Insurance Company (TDIC) have employee manuals specific for dentistry. Other companies specific for dentists include CEDR HR www.cedrhrsolutions.com, Human Resource Advisors www.humanresourceadvisors.com and HR for Health www.hrforhealth.com.

All of these forms will be stored in each team member's personnel folder along with regular performance notes and annual reviews. Update information periodically and keep personnel folders locked. These files contain confidential information. You may want to store these folders off-site or scan personnel records so that they can be kept securely and never lost or stolen. You may want to store all of your HR information electronically.

Chapter 6

PROFESSIONAL APPEARANCE

You can't teach employees to smile.
They have to smile before you hire them.
– Arte Nathan

I once asked a cast member at Walt Disney World, "How is it that all of the cast members at the park look so good?" The cast member replied, "It's easy. If we don't look good, up to the standards of the Disney Corporation Team Handbook, we get sent home."

It's Showtime! From the second you walk into your dental office and see your first patient of the day, you're on. Dress for success. There are many things that convey professionalism. Dress code is one of them. Take the time to dress to look trustworthy, clean, and smart. Requirements for professional appearance in the dental office will need to be written in your Team Handbook, stated, accepted, reviewed, maintained and enforced, over and over again for your entire professional career. This quest never ends.

Why is dress code important? The unconscious mind makes a judgment about professional appearance in a matter of seconds. The patient sees a doctor and team image, which consists of many things. You know professional appearance when you see it. It instantly builds confidence in the doctor and the team and puts patients at ease. Professional appearance builds patient trust.

Appearance is not frequently discussed. In an instant, it reflects to the patient the quality of the dental treatment and attention to detail of the office. Being well dressed also transmits a high level of responsibility and respect for the patients. Maintaining a respectable dress code is an important aspect of HR management and worth your time and attention.

CLEAN AND HEALTHY –

Convey an image which expresses dental health and general wellbeing. Appearing confident and happy will put your dental patients at ease. As healthcare professionals, we ourselves must portray what we are trying to achieve for our patients, that is, overall wellness and dental health.

Along with body cleanliness, all tattoos need to be covered either by clothing or bandages. Hair and nails need to be clean. Clothing should also be clean and without rips, stains, or wrinkles.

The body posture and expressions of everyone in the dental office should convey health. The team should be adequately rested for work, without yawns, poor posture, tired attitudes, or sleepiness. Physical health and mental health should be conveyed.

GREAT TEETH AND FRESH BREATH –

A beautiful smile is one of the most attractive aspects of one's appearance. Gorgeous smiles will make your dental office most welcoming and memorable. You work in a dental office. Your teeth and smile need to be great and your breath fresh. This is, after all, what you provide and are encouraging your patients to attain for themselves. *When you frequently smile for your dental patients, you need to have attractive, healthy, straight, white teeth.* This is especially true for the dentist.

Watch what you eat for lunch when working in a dental office. Garlic or baloney can really produce a bad case of after-lunch halitosis. Even though we wear facemasks as we provide dentistry to our dental patients, our mouths are very close to the patient's nose. Encourage your team to tell you and each other should something be stuck between someone's teeth after lunch. Take time to brush your teeth after lunch and have fresh breath. Use mouthwash, breath mints, breath spray, and don't forget to scrape your tongue. But be sure not to chew gum in the dental office. Chewing gum is very unprofessional.

Offer free dentistry and orthodontic treatment to your dental team to eliminate yellow, crooked teeth. Be sure the dental team and doctor look great. Make your smile the best it can be.

GOOD HAIR –

When working with dental patients, long hair needs to be pulled back so as to not go in the patient's face or in the dentist's or assistant's face. Hair should be neat and clean. You also want your hair always dry when starting your workday. Hair needs to look appealing and well groomed. Wet, highly gelled, spiked, or wildly colored hair is not desirable for the dental office and could actually scare patients away!

GOOD POSTURE –

Take care of your back. As dentists and dental assistants, we have a tendency to lean over chairside for a long part of the workday. Watch your posture! Preserve your back! Straight posture is a sign of a great attitude, work engagement, motivation, and enthusiasm for the dental office job. Attention to ergonomics in the dental professional will help work longevity, with fewer back problems and less neck pain. Adjust your equipment settings and positions for maximum comfort. Take time to stretch and straighten up.

CLASSY AND PROFESSIONAL –

Dental team members are best advised to look classy and professional in dress and demeanor. Save sexy for the Friday nightclub. Clothing must be in good condition, pressed or ironed. Coordinated uniforms provided by the office are best for a put-together and unified professional look for the team.

PROFESSIONAL SHOES –

Shoes must be clean and polished without excessive scuffmarks. Colors white, black, or brown are most professional. Leather is best for dental assisting not only for durability but also for safety. Consider flat rubber-soled shoes for all-day comfort. If you work at the front desk, a moderate-heeled business pump can also be worn.

Save your sneakers for the playground. Sneakers look unprofessional. Avoid shoes that are cloth or have a bold wacky pattern or design.

STOCKINGS AND SOCKS –

Wear socks, please! Even if you work in a dental office in Miami Beach, Florida, stockings or socks are required. This is an OSHA requirement. It would be unprofessional and unhygienic not to have stockings, no matter how hot it might be outside. This applies especially to the doctor. Save your sandals for the beach.

Wear clean socks and avoid white socks. As your patients sit in the dental chair, they will look down toward the floor and see your shoes and socks. Have them reflect the quality of your dental treatment and your office.

If you are a dental professional at the front desk and wear a skirt, avoid wild fishnet stockings. This also applies to the doctor. Keep your office appearance as professional as possible. Dress for success.

SLACKS –

Slacks should be pressed and hemmed to a professional length, with a break above the instep in front and above the heel in the back. Pant legs should touch just to the heel of the shoe and not trail on the floor. Preferred colors for dental assistant pants are white, khaki, or black with a professional top. Color-coordinated scrubs may also be worn. Many dental offices provide scrubs in an assortment of matching colors.

Doctors, do wear dress pants and avoid jeans and chinos. Forget the "Casual Friday" look. We are in a service industry seeing new patients each and every day of the week. You need to always look your best.

WHITE COAT –

We once asked our patients in a questionnaire "Should the doctor wear scrubs?" Unless doing the surgery, the overwhelming response was "No!" Results of studies have shown that patients prefer to see their doctor well dressed and wearing a white coat. The white coat with the doctor name connotes professionalism in the dental profession.

The University of Queensland School of Medicine, and the Ochsner

Clinic Foundation in New Orleans did a study to ask patients what they preferred for their doctor to wear, choosing from traditional white coat, bare-below-the-elbow attire (scrub top), a white coat with scrubs, and scrubs alone. Respondents rated images head-to-head for their preference. Overall, 69.9% of the 153 patients surveyed preferred doctors to wear white coats. Patients disliked scrub tops, scoring them the very lowest on the patient comfort and confidence scales.

Dr. S. Mark Hong wrote in *Dental Economics:* "Scrubs are cheap, disposable, and look sloppy. Scrubs are the dental equivalent of a T-shirt and jeans." Even if you are a periodontist or an oral surgeon, when doing a new patient exam, a white shirt and tie still shows respect. To show respect for your patients, to build their comfort level and to promote confidence in their care in your dental office, doctor, please put on the white coat.

CASE STUDY 8: "THE SLACKER"

Hilda bought a pair of khaki slacks as part of her office uniform. The first day she worn them, the doctor and HR manager told Hilda that the bottom of her slacks were dragging on the floor. Hilda did not seem to mind. After several days of asking Hilda to hem her pants, the doctor and HR manager offered to hem Hilda's slacks for her in an effort to get the job done. Hilda was told to leave her slacks at the office and they would hem them for her, something easily done at the dry cleaners for low cost. She did not do so. At this point, hemming became a team effort.

Finally, at the next full team meeting, every team member was told that if their slacks were not hemmed in one week's time, they would be asked to go home.

Hilda then quit. The doctor and HR manager were perplexed. Why wouldn't Hilda hem her slacks? The response came. Hilda liked to go dancing on Friday nights with platform shoes and she wanted to wear her long work slacks to the club!

ACTION:

If someone's dress standards are not up to the standards of your office, something needs to be done immediately. You will need to speak one-on-one and to the entire group in fairness to get the job done before sending someone home for dress-code violation.

You will face attention-to-detail dress challenges when it comes to maintaining a dress code of professional appearance. Each person is individual and unique; getting everyone on the team to agree to a standard dress code will be a challenge. Millennials in particular are used to "dressing down." Unless you want your office to have an appearance of "casual chic," a dress code is something which needs constant attention and maintenance.

It is not the HR manager's intention to single anyone out. When a problem arises, the rules apply fairly to all team members. Standards need to be maintained across the board.

This story of the Slacker may sound ridiculous. Don't be surprised when something ridiculous arises in your dental office pertaining to dress code. Human beings are complex. Sometimes these displays are a bit out of line. Be prepared to talk about dress code.

BLAZERS AND SUITS –
No dress connotes professionalism more than a suit or pantsuit with a blazer. Always look professional at the front desk and when asking for payment for expensive dental procedures; this polished look of success may help your office treatment coordinator start the case. Suits give the front-desk receptionist or the treatment coordinator the look of responsibility and respect. This is especially important when dealing with financial transactions. Suits also look professional for continuing education courses outside of the office. Dressing up in a suit or blazer always represents your dental office well.

BUSINESS CASUAL –
As representatives of your dental office, you need to look respectable. This especially applies to clothing worn to courses and meetings outside of your office in the community among your referring colleagues. At continuing education courses and professional meetings, team members will be interacting with others and giving an impression about your office. You want this impression to be favorable. Miniskirts, fishnet stockings, spiked heels, and spaghetti straps are to be avoided. We're aiming for country-club appearance, not disco-club appearance. Team members, after all, attend professional meetings to learn, not to leave and go to a disco or county fair.

The doctors, in general, should always look their best. Even if the doctor is residing outside of the practice community, you never know when you might run into a patient at the shopping plaza. It is always recommended to look as good as possible.

SHIRTS –

Wear a shirt or blouse, not too tight, not too loose, no cleavage showing. Leave the push-up bra from Victoria's Secret at home. Pressed or ironed, make sure your shirt is not see-through (diaphanous). We want our patients focusing on dentistry while in our dental office, not underwear!

Doctors, do wear quality dress shirts or blouses at the office. Men look most professional in a high thread-count shirt with a professional collar. Avoid the button-down collars and rolling up your sleeves. A good tie will complete the professional look. Ties with a solid repeating pattern are always the best, understated choice.

NAMETAGS –

A nametag must be worn at all times when treating patients in the dental office as an OSHA standard. Emily Post in The Etiquette Daily states that your nametag is properly worn on ***the right side*** of your upper chest below the shoulder so that the person shaking hands or greeting has easy eye contact with both the person and the nametag. The doctor's name can be embroidered on the doctor's white jacket. For dental auxiliaries, the nametag lists first name and position. Patients and visitors will refer to your nametag often as they get to know the doctor and the team.

FINGERNAILS –

For hygiene and the comfort of the dental patient, nails need to be clean, short and natural. The test for dental-healthcare professional nail length is to turn your palm over and not see your nails. This length of nails ensures that the dentist and the assistants do not stab the patient in the gums when completing dental procedures in the mouth. No acrylic nails, glued-on nails, nail art, or outrageous colors. Natural-looking nails are always best.

JEWELRY –
Minimal jewelry should be worn in the dental office. As dentists and dental assistants, we *wash our hands between each patient encounter.* It is not practical or hygienic to wear multiple pieces of jewelry, especially on the hands. Nothing too massive can be worn under gloves.

One set of earrings that look professional is desired. Tongue rings, eyebrow rings, and nose rings do not comply with the dental office brand of health. Assistants who show up for work with unprofessional piercings will be asked to remove the jewelry immediately before starting work. Otherwise, they will be asked to go home. Be aware that although multiple pieces of jewelry or piercings may be appropriate at a rock concert or in the motorcycle world, these items do not convey a feeling of gentleness, kindness, comfort, health, and wellness to the dental patient.

FITNESS AND REST –
No yawns, please. Members of a dental team need to be physically fit. This will help you handle being on your feet, sitting and standing, up and down, back and forth, several times per day. Team members cannot appear tired or immobile when treating patients.

Rest and mental fitness can minimize complaining and negativity. Dental team members need stamina to be energetic, positive, active and capable of offering outstanding customer service and a great patient experience. Your positive energy needs to last all day.

> *You're never fully dressed without a smile.*
> – Annie Oakley

YOUR FACE –
Put a smile on your face and not too much makeup. Your smile will reflect your positive energy and great attitude. Even with your facemask on, you will be smiling with your eyes. Watch not to have too much perfume or aftershave, and no visible tattoos. Be attractive, pleasant, pretty, handsome, and natural. Everything about your appearance should be clean and in good condition, reflective of overall health.

Having a good sense of humor, good disposition, and being happy will make your face look great. Be thankful for having a great job treating wonderful patients. Make your patient's day. Make every patient feel like the most important patient that day. Smile!

Let your mantra be, "Dress for success." In return, your professional appearance will earn you, your dental team, and the doctor respect and patient confidence in your dental care. You may become known as the best-dressed, most professional office in town. Patients may refer more patients to you, and your office may earn a great reputation by letting patients know through your appearance and demeanor that your dental office has got it together and is the to-go place for the best dental care in town.

Chapter 7

PROFESSIONAL CONDUCT

Ethics and character count.
Always respect the doctor/patient relationship.
– Anonymous

I n order to deliver the best customer service and patient experience possible, we all need to occasionally be reminded of habits to eliminate to make our conduct as excellent and professional as possible. It takes courage to maintain a high standard of conduct among your dental team. The doctor, first and foremost, needs to set a good example. It's important to maintain an office culture including ethics, integrity, character, and respect for the doctor/patient relationship.

Potential new patients will make a judgment about the doctor, the team and the office environment within the first seven seconds of entering your reception room. What feeling does your office communicate? Perceived actions must be seen as respectful, kind, gentle, and professional. Words heard from the doctor and team must be conveyed in a professional tone to build trust and to convince the new patients that they want to be treated at your dental office.

Employees must always strive to maintain professionalism at all times. They may sign a pledge of patient confidentiality stated in the Team Handbook. It is our ultimate goal of service to the patient to honor the doctor/patient relationship and the office/patient relationship.

The day-to-day working environment of your dental office may be as important as the doctor's diagnosis, treatment plan, and dental treatment. Patient communication, both verbal and nonverbal, must create patient ease and confidence.

To help team members improve and maintain a high standard of conduct, it is important to review two important topics: courtesy and etiquette. These are two of the most important signs of professionalism.

COURTESY –

Everyone in the dental office needs to focus his or her attention fully on the patient. Courtesy includes saying, "please, thank you, my pleasure, and you're welcome." It is important to be polite and treat others the way you would like to be treated, and, more importantly, the way they would like to be treated. One way to give others respect is to put their needs above your own.

Courtesy and customer service is especially needed in the dental office around lunchtime and at closing hours. Discussion then needs to stay focused on the patient, not the time or personal lunch schedules. Workday breaks and the schedule are not the concern of the patient, regardless of the time. The patient deserves your full attention until their dental visit is done. You are employed in the dental office to serve and care for the patient.

Smiling and not rushing will put the patient at ease. Focus your full attention on the patient in front of you. Show respect for them in every way. Make your dental patient the most important person in the room. Take the time to know what is special in each one of your patients.

ETIQUETTE –

Etiquette may be defined as what is proper, refined, polite, and respectful in Western culture. Etiquette includes use of proper English and professional language such as "yes, excuse me, please repeat." Slang and poor English language is off-limits in a professional dental office. Slang is sloppy and disrespectful to those who must hear it. This applies to those who speak second languages as well.

To create a pleasant and relaxed dental environment, watch what you discuss with patients. Avoid discussion of religion, politics, unpleasant current events, and especially personal problems, office repairs, lunch and quitting time.

Etiquette includes good posture, eye contact, smiling and speaking slowly, calmly, and clearly to the patient. Adjust your speed to be in synchrony with your patients. Help your patients whenever possible in whatever way you can. Consider yourself a dental concierge.

Go the extra mile to make the office look beautiful for the comfort of your dental patient. Always keep the dental office clean and tidy. Leave countertops cleared as much as possible. Be sure to clean up after yourself, after each dental procedure, and activity in the office. Clean the carpets and have a deep clean at least once per year.

Take time to introduce yourself to new patients and new visitors in your dental office. Say hello to anyone who passes within ten feet of where you are working no matter what your job. Give your business card to new patients and tell them to call you personally if you can help them in any way. Collect business cards of those you meet and make a point of remembering their names as well and a few facts about them. You may want to list patient interests and preferences in your patient chart.

Rather than pointing, walk your patient to their next destination within the dental office. Ask the patient if they would like a magazine or blanket when they are initially seated in your dental chair. Ask how you could make them as comfortable as possible. For long procedures, give your patient a comfort break.

Go the extra mile of customer service for your dental patients by scheduling additional dental appointments and specialist appointments for them. Facilitate their comprehensive dental treatment. Help your patients achieve maximum dental health as easily and quickly as possible. Be an active member of their dental health team.

Electronic Etiquette –

Cell phones should be put away while at work. Review your dental office policy regarding electronic devices in the dental office. In order to be in compliance with HIPAA, all photography must be in the form of controlled pictures to maintain patient confidentiality in the dental office. *Recording and "Selfies" are strictly prohibited in the dental office, as they pick up background confidential patient information and violate HIPAA.*

VERBAL ETIQUETTE –

In the movie "My Fair Lady," a British shop girl is turned into a high-fashion lady of society with a little help of a caring professor who improves her language and dresses her up. Often, dentists or HR managers may find themselves in the same situation in the dental office, working on grammar and professional dress and behavior with a new team member. "Books cannot be judged by their covers." Someone's talent and performance may not be adequately reflected by their outward appearance and common speech. Appearance and speech are easily improved. Talent, IQ, and performance are not.

Each day we all strive to be the best we can be. Adhering to etiquette is just another way that we can show attention to detail and respect for our dental patients. By this, we build their confidence in the quality of the care and dental treatment that we provide.

CASE STUDY 9: "MY FAIR LADY"

Terri was a fabulous technical dental assistant. She performed all front-desk functions meticulously and was pleasant, smiled, and had a GREAT attitude. There was only one problem. Terri's English language was a little "rough around the edges." It was primitive and did not reflect her attention to detail, job performance, or level of care of the dental office. English was her primary language, and Terri was a U.S. high school graduate. Yet, it was a bit surprising that she commonly made grammatical errors when speaking.

Often Terri would say "Yeah" instead of "Yes" and "Huh" rather than "Please repeat." She started sentences with "Me and you" instead of "You and I" and referred to the office personnel as "You guys" rather than "we" or "the team."

This casual language was common in the community where Terri lived and at the high school that she attended. Her grammar was not reflective of her level of intelligence or the professionalism of her service or outstanding patient care that she delivered in the dental office.

It needed a little work to well reflect the professionalism of her dental office.

ACTION:

Grammar can be worked on and improved. It is possible to take an English grammar class or a speech class at a local junior college. Grammar just takes practice. It's simple to teach team members grammar and review proper grammar and polite phrases at team meetings. Scripts can be written, phrases practiced. "My pleasure, I'll be happy to, You're welcome, Please, and Thank You" are a few phrases. "Yes" and "You and I" are two more.

I once had a fabulous waiter serve me in a café at a resort in Carmel, California. He was originally from Mexico and English was his second language. He had been in the country only a short time but his English grammar, courtesy and etiquette were impeccable. I was so impressed. I asked him how he learned the English language so well in such a short period of time. He told me he had married a woman originally from Germany. English was also her second language. Together, they had worked on their language skills, every day, by repeating polite phrases and memorizing the rules of grammar. This left a big impression on me that everyone in the dental office could and should be able to improve their English language skills in the same way for the benefit of the patients whom we serve. We can all sound professional and courteous in an effort to deliver outstanding customer service.

ELECTRONIC ETIQUETTE –

We now enter a new age of electronic etiquette in the dental office. It must be stated that while there are patients in the office, it is disrespectful to be on cell phones, taking personal calls, on the Internet, on Facebook, or "just checking in." While at work, personal cell phones need to be stored in lockers, not in uniform pockets. This also goes for the doctor. Our patients deserve our full attention. Think of your dental office as a surgical operating room. There are no cell phones in an OR. Likewise, our dental patients and procedures require 100% of our undivided attention.

Chapter 8

PROFESSIONAL DEVELOPMENT

There is no I in team,
but there is in win.
— Michael Jordan

When the 1992 United States Men's Olympic basketball team was chosen, they put together a group of outstanding individuals: Michael Jordan, Scottie Pippen, John Stockton, Karl Malone, Magic Johnson, Larry Bird, Patrick Ewing, Chris Mullin, David Robinson, and Charles Barkley. They were all selected at the peaks of their NBA careers. Christian Laettner from Duke University was only college player invited to the team. He performed alongside the professional players, despite his age and inexperience.

Jordan was the only player who studied the opposition, carefully watching game tapes. The closest of the eight matches was Team USA's 117-85 victory over Croatia in the gold medal game. *Sports Illustrated* later stated that the Dream Team was "arguably the most dominant squad ever assembled in any sport." Bird called the Olympic gold medal ceremony "the ultimate experience." Johnson said, "The '92 Dream Team was the greatest moment of my life." Jordan said that the biggest benefit for him from the Olympics was that he learned more about his teammates' weaknesses. He later defeated Barkley's, Malone's, and Stockton's teams in three NBA finals.

Scientific studies have shown that individuals work better and at a higher level of performance output on individual tasks than in teams. Those who work alone and are responsible for the outcome and results of their own work most often give a 100% effort. You might think that being on a team would maximize output so that $1 + 1 + 1 = 3$ or maybe even $1 + 1 + 1 = 4$, but this is actually not the case. When individuals without personal responsibility work as a group in a team effort, total output is realistically closer to $1 + 1 + 1 = 2.53$. This work theory has been carefully studied and scientifically proven using the model of crew-team rowers and rope pullers.

By giving your dental team members an opportunity to work and excel on their own projects or to "pull their own weight," they individually will develop their own unique dental career talents, skills and achievements. High-accomplishment individuals will contribute and produce a highly productive and effective team.

I love getting to know people, helping people, and seeing them develop and succeed. It's what I love most about human resource management. Like some of you, I have had my HRM challenges and difficulties, and some real "rehabilitation projects." But the hard work, problem solving, improvements, and successes along the way have been perhaps the most rewarding aspect of my dental career as an orthodontist.

I have one piece of advice I can give from 25 years of dental office management experience: evaluate the results produced. Individual performance counts. Keep score. You can always dress someone to look professional, educate them on procedures, coach their verbal skills and improve their grammar. Independent of these simple things are results. If you have results, you have the most precious and important talent of all.

To keep everyone motivated and engaged in their dental careers as dental professionals, have personal projects and report on this progress at team meetings. Make each assistant an office champion of their own area of expertise. At monthly meetings, take the time to listen to individual reports on project progress. Enjoy and witness the individual pride and fulfillment in the presentations. Implement the full engagement of each person in the office. Give everyone an opportunity to speak and to express their opinions and suggestions, hopes, and dreams for the office. This is the best advice you will ever get for your dental office.

Everyone will enjoy freedom to develop and grow within their own personal dental career, the same way dentists do with theirs. By reading books and going to courses to gain new knowledge, everyone stays enthusiastic about their dental career and the dental office. Certification classes and fellowships offer great achievement goals. You may even want to hold CE classes and group meetings in your office for the dental community.

In an orthodontic office, team members may wear many hats for special functions. These job descriptions may include:

1. Treatment Coordinator
2. Patient Coordinator
3. Insurance Coordinator
4. Collection Coordinator
5. Records Coordinator
6. Invisalign Coordinator
7. Public Relations Coordinator
8. Computer Specialist
9. Social Media Specialist
10. Supply Coordinator
11. Human Resource Manager
12. Office Manager
13. Assistant Office Manager
14. Huddle Leader
15. Greeter and Concierge
16. Customer Service Coordinator

You may want to consider titles or areas of special interest for your dental office team champions. Make up some of your own. These could include Implant Coordinator or Denture Receptionist. Whatever you and your team decide, giving individual responsibility and autonomy will foster individual pride and high performance.

Michael Jordan couldn't score every point on the Dream Team. Sometimes he had to pass the ball to Larry Bird. Although you should strive to give every person at least one special area of expertise, cross-training and being willing to "pitch in" are essential, too. In times of sickness or vacation leave, team members will need to fill in. "That's not in my job description" should never be heard in a high-performance dental office. All team members should be able to handle and fix any office problem which may arise most often on their own. "If you see it you own it" is a great mantra for tackling a problem and seeing it through for immediate service recovery.

CASE STUDY 10: "THE WILLING"

Patti started out in sterilization at minimum wage. As a single teen mother, she had completed her GED and gone to junior college for dental assisting in her thirties. When she was done with her daily duties of sterilization, she would go to the front desk and ask if she could help the office manager with filing. The office manager started giving Patti new projects. All projects were finished accurately and in a timely manner. When a front-desk Patient Coordinator left her job position, the Office Manager stated that she would rather have Patti at the front desk with her than any of the candidates interviewed from a Craigslist job-opening announcement.

Patti started billing insurance. She soon mastered that job. Soon she was trained in and performing all front-desk functions well. Eventually, the Office Manager moved to another city. Patti took over at the front desk as Office Manager. She worked forty hours per week and took care of all office emergencies, even a water pipe break on the weekend when the doctor was away.

Patti was dedicated and dependable. Her excellent performance earned her a raise every year. She was a valued and trusted team member. In a short time, she had achieved the highest compensation possible in dentistry for a dental assistant. With her increased income she soon bought her first home. Then a new and larger-scale office position opened in a multi-doctor multi-practice group practice in a nearby community. The new position had exceptional corporate benefits. Patti decided she would go for the job. She got it. Patti left her first dental office of nine years on good terms to continue her personal development.

ACTION:
Patti is a dentistry career-development success story. This is why we love dentistry and the people with whom we work. Everyone loves a winner and a winning attitude.

Part Three

TEAM MANAGEMENT

Effective leaders don't say "I."
They don't think "I."
They think "we"; they think "team."
They understand their job to be to make the team function.
They accept responsibility, but "we" gets the credit.
This is what creates trust, what enables you to get the task done.
– Peter F. Drucker

D ental teams span generations. In today's workforce, we are challenged with the integration of Baby Boomers (born from 1946–64), Generation Xers (born 1965–77), and Generation Yers or Millennials (born 1978–96) all working together. All generations of team members are products of six major value-shaping influences that impact their lives: family, education, morality, peers, spirituality, and culture. Past generations lived to work. The younger generations work to live.

Millennials add a new team balance to the dental office. Excellent with computers, the majority of Millennials are great assets to our dental teams. Millennials bring many fresh values to the dental office environment, including work-life balance, rewards, creativity, computer skills, informality, simplicity, multitasking and new meaning. Millennials embrace diversity and make the office fun. Often, they are very comfortable with teamwork and great members of the dental team.

When it comes to HRM, there will be many times when you will be managing the resolution of human conflicts. It may be your own human conflict with performance expectations. Conflicts may thus be between the doctor and the team, between team members, or regarding patient concerns. These are the situations which will need your leadership for immediate resolution. Conflicts will need analysis, time and attention, thought, and tender loving care for their solution and resolution. They will need courage to address, and candor to resolve.

Conflicts may be personality conflicts. Most can be resolved through communication, trust, and understanding. Should you not address the personality-conflict problem, or you avoid it completely, it will continue to fester like an open wound and it will continue to affect your office teamwork and ultimately, the success of your dental practice.

To eliminate conflict, and to build communication, empathy, and trust, start by getting the entire team together socially, outside of the dental office. Schedule a team outing. Take a morning off and go bowling. Let team members socialize, let down their guard, talk about themselves, their families, and their feelings. Watch the camaraderie and teamwork grow!

Relationships need to be built for a great group of individuals to succeed working together. The happiest employees have a best friend at work. For a great team to function effectively, each team member needs to communicate freely and each voice and opinion heard. Most of all, each member of a dental team needs to like and respect the other members as well as the doctor. In return, the doctor must respect and appreciate each member of the team and treat him or her as a professional.

If your office does not have an environment of professional communication and teamwork, it will be more difficult for your office goals to be reached. Your office environment may be a bit toxic. Such an environment will have tension, or the feeling of "walking on egg shells." Mediate communication tensions to keep them from festering. There may be jealousy. There may be turf wars and resentment. Find the root of the problem and resolve it. Put a solution in place.

CASE STUDY 11: "The Millennial"

Betty was a Millennial. She was raised as an only child in a well-off home with two working parents. She had received a lot of attention and praise her entire life. Married now with a small child of her own, she utilized her own parents for continued help and childcare. After her child started school, Betty decided to enter the workforce as a registered dental assistant.

Betty began to work at a dental office front desk. The dental office she joined was well established, and Betty's teammates were career veterans who already worked well together, in perfect harmony. Within a few weeks, Betty started to express how she would like to be treated differently. She described the work and job duties that she would like to do and not to do. She also expressed that she would like to move up the ladder as quickly as possible.

After being on the job for a few weeks, it was soon discovered that Betty's mother still balanced her personal checkbook. This was concerning to the office manager and doctor considering that Betty was in a position of responsibility of collecting money and making bank deposits for the practice.

Betty also seemed to be irritated by her assigned tasks at the front desk. Her duties were perceived as banal and some work requests seemed "below her." One day, frustrated by her work, Betty stamped her feet declaring, "I can't do this … I can't do this …" while everyone looked on in disbelief and amazement at the spectacle they saw before them. A few weeks later, she entered the private office of the doctor under the "open door policy" to complain that she didn't enjoy the limitations of her job, and didn't like one of her co-workers.

When the doctor tried to explain to Betty that she needed to express a positive attitude of service, cooperation and teamwork, Betty informed the doctor that he was "giving *her* attitude"! At that moment, the doctor determined that, plain and simple, Betty could not be coached and was not a fit for the practice.

After being given a verbal warning and an opportunity to improve, Betty quit within the next few weeks to work for another dental office. This new office did not call for a reference. After causing upheaval and disharmony in that dental office, Betty quit that office within a short period of time as well. Soon, she left the dental profession altogether.

ACTION:
Tell the Millennial that *everyone who works for the practice* is expected to work well with others, to complete her tasks, and to be part of the office culture and team. Point out what desirable work behaviors are and give her an opportunity to improve. Explain that it is your job to help the Millennial succeed in the office and work culture that you have in place. Explain to the Millennial, that for her success in the dental office she needs to perform, be trusted and respectful, and get along well with oth-

ers on the team, and the doctor as well.

We all want to foster an amazing and supportive work environment that promotes the success of each team member. We want each team member to achieve his or her dreams. And, we want to be supportive of each team member as a person. We may have team members who themselves want to go to dental school and are capable of everything. Nothing could make us more happy or proud. Anything is possible.

Chapter 9

THE SCHEDULE

Let us realize that:
the privilege to work is a gift,
the power to work is a blessing,
the love of work is success!
— David O. McKay

A doctor's ideal day is not necessarily a team member's ideal day. Dentists tend to be focused on the bottom line, the daily production and collections within the office. They are most content and feel happy and calm with a full schedule. When a dentist walks into their office and sees a packed schedule they will say, "It is going to be a great day!"

Often, a team member's vision of an ideal day is different. The team member's response to a packed schedule may be "AH! It's going to be a really tough day!" When seeing a completely full schedule some dental assistants may be freaked out, bummed out, or even upset!

It's up to the doctor and office manager to determine the ideal number of patients and procedures in terms of performance and production for the perfect day. This daily scheduling goal can then be reviewed, understood, and accepted by all team members.

Occasionally, the workday may have a few open appointments and cancellations. Some team members may look at these openings and say, "It's going to be a great day!" The dentist, on the other hand, will be upset with cancellations and worried about the lack of production and financial burden of an empty schedule. The doctor may decide to send a few team members home. Thus is the Yin and Yang of daily appointment scheduling, and push and pull between the dentist and the team.

It makes financial sense for a dentist without a full schedule to send a few dental assistants home. Yet this is rarely done. The assistants, after all, are hired to assist the doctor with patient dental procedures. If there are no patients, there is no work for them. This needs to be clearly understood. This will make everyone appreciate a full schedule all the more. The doctor may quickly find the front desk coordinators encouraged by the back office team looking for ways to actively fill the schedule.

To realize an ideal day in the dental office, each individual assistant may have her own column of patients at her own chair with her own responsibility for starting and finishing each procedure with the doctor on time. The dentist may want to specify the number of patients seen daily in each chair. In this way, the dentist may also want to have each assistant responsible for chair production and, like a hygienist, call unscheduled patients to fill her chair column for the day.

You will need to determine what daily management style works best for your dental office, in terms of ideal production, efficiency, and happiness. This may change from month to month, quarter to quarter, or year to year. You may choose to have days be different for each day of the week or different days of the month or altered for seasonal times of the year. Hours may need to be expanded or contracted depending on the ever-changing numbers of new and existing patients.

You may want to evaluate schedule needs quarterly to decide what HR efficiency changes could be made. Perhaps you could hire part-time assistants to work the busiest times of the week or the day. HR costs are the highest overhead expense in the dental office. A full schedule with a matching number of assistants will keep these overhead costs ideal and under control.

Properly managing the hours and minutes that each of your team members work can save thousands of dollars in HR costs per year. I am not suggesting you constantly cut back or try to take work hours away. What I am suggesting is that your office be open the proper number of hours each week to serve the patient needs that you have and that attention be paid to hire team members to work your schedule needs while finishing each day on time, with attention to overtime. Just a few employees working a little overtime every day or week will add up to thousands of extra dollars each year in unnecessary HR costs.

HOURS OF OPERATION

Most dental offices are open 8 hours per day, 5 days a week. You may want to schedule 1 ½ hours lunch, and allot time for 15 minutes for setup and 15 minutes of clean up to avoid frequent overtime expense. This gives team members time to complete tasks without exceeding eight hours.

Even if the doctor is out of the office at a conference or on a day off, the phones are still best answered eight hours per day, five days per week, including lunchtime. Most busy working professionals make their personal phone calls at lunchtime. It is especially important that the phones are answered during this time.

Staggering lunches will keep the phone lines open without creating overtime or break issues for a single employee. It is possible to hire someone who would start work at 11:30 a.m. and specifically answer the phones during the noontime hour. In California, if an employee works through lunch without taking their mandatory half-hour break after four hours, they are owed an extra hour of premium pay for that time. Overtime at time and a half would be paid for all time over eight hours. However you work out lunchtime phone coverage, giving attention to new patient calls during this important time of the day will certainly help your practice grow.

Mondays are also an important day of new calls to the dentist. Potential new patients have spent the weekend thinking about their dental needs or even worse, are in some type of need or discomfort. Even if your office is usually closed on Mondays, have a phone receptionist available on Mondays to schedule new patient exams for the rest of the week.

An evening emergency phone number is also required by the dental board of each dental office. Emergency calls need to be taken by the doctor. A home number, cell number, or pager number may be left on the office answering machine. The doctor when reached can render advice over the phone, meet the patient in the office, or refer to another dental specialist for emergency dental procedures.

If you need additional help with phone answering, there are professional dental phone services. Take time to research local providers or national phone answering services such as Dental Support Specialties: www.dentalsupportspecialties.com.

Meal period

While there are not federal laws that require lunch breaks, a few states such as California require a half-hour meal period break after five hours of work. The meal period can be sooner than five hours, but no later. This is true even if there is a "Lunch and Learn." Even if lunch is being served, employees must clock out and take a half-hour break after five hours of work. *If the team member is not offered a half-hour meal period after five hours and work continues on, then the half-hour meal period is to be paid plus 1 hour of additional premium pay and any overtime caused by the time worked at time and one-half.*

Overtime

Pre-authorization from the doctor or office manager for a team member staying late in the office can prevent overtime. Have a preauthorization policy explicitly stated in your Team Handbook, with pre-authorization slips ready for signature. These slips can include the overtime limit for that day, for example one hour or two hours. Repeated abuse of overtime not preauthorized is grounds for dismissal. Be sure *not* to create circumstances of policies that would imply that unauthorized overtime will not be paid. Be sure to always pay overtime when it is owed. *Paying overtime is the law.*

CASE STUDY 12: "The Overtime Queen"

Elizabeth needed to catch up on some dental insurance billing. She was a salaried employee of nonexempt status. She asked the doctor if she could stay after hours to complete her insurance billing work. Assuming that Elizabeth's request was for one hour, the doctor verbally said "Yes," without specifying any time period or limit agreement.

After the full eight-hour day, Elizabeth stayed at work until eleven p.m. The doctor was obligated to pay an additional six hours of overtime at time and one-half. Elizabeth did this every day, every week for one month before the doctor realized what was going on. By the end-of-the-month payday, the overtime added up to an extra cost of $1,500 in over-time for Elizabeth.

The doctor then terminated Elizabeth for overtime abuse. Elizabeth was not happy since she felt that she had been given verbal approval by the doctor for her to stay late to bill insurance. She filed for unemployment and complained to the state unemployment office that she was fired in retaliation for receiving overtime pay. The dental office then received a state investigation for overtime with a requirement for review of every single employee in the practice for the last two years. It was then determined that the doctor owed Elizabeth and other employees even more money. The doctor then received the mandate for additional wages and penalties. These included payback for overtime and numerous penalties for failure to pay overtime in a timely manner. These monetary penalties included failure to pay all wages at termination and failure to provide the required overtime wage information on the paycheck wage statement.

ACTION:
Always pay overtime when it is due. It is the law. Overtime is best preapproved in writing with a duration period and ending time as outlined in the Team Handbook. It appears that the misunderstanding in this case as determined by the unemployment office was the doctor's fault. Have a preauthorization system in place for overtime and assign the desired hours of overtime, when needed, in writing. Set a limit. Always keep accurate records and accurate payroll accounting on wage statements, including overtime hours and pay.

Salaried employees considered "exempt" without overtime must qualify for this status. An exempt employee is a high-level administrator or office manager. Merely paying someone a salary does not guarantee that they are truly categorized as exempt and not qualified for overtime.

The Fair Labor Standards Act (FLSA) rules for exempt vs. nonexempt status are specific. The FLSA exempts broad categories of "white collar" jobs such as doctors, executives, and high level managers, from overtime requirements by exempt status. In the dental office, things become more questionable. In order for salaried managers to be classified as exempt from federal overtime rules, the employee must pass three tests:

1. They must be paid a minimum of $455/week.
2. They must have a fixed salary. *Any day the exempt employee works they must be paid their full salary.*
3. The employee must meet the duties of an administrator, executive, or professional. Exempt vs. Non-exempt status and overtime are

79

often at the center of many IRS and DOL audits. Should you have an exempt employee, it will still be necessary to track their hours or possibly pay them overtime. Do a self-audit of your exempt status employee and document your efforts. Make this part of your HR review process. You can learn more about exempt employee status and find an AUDIT checklist at CEDR Solutions: www.cedrsolutions.com/exempt-vs-non-exemptstatus. Remember that state-to-state, these rules may also change.

BIRTHDAY PARTIES

Doctors and business owners do a lot of planning for the office and the team. Doctors plan the big things. Let team members have some autonomy at planning the little things. This would include birthday parties. Birthday parties and celebrations in general should not be on the clock and it must be clear that attendance at birthday parties is not mandatory.

Some doctors may want to take the team out for a special lunch or special gathering after work if the office is small. These are not paid events. Bigger offices may celebrate the birthdays of all the team members in a given month on one specific day. It is also possible to have the person with the last birthday plan the party for the team member with the next birthday. Spread the love and the process of party planning between everyone. This gives everyone something to look forward to, and makes the office fun.

SPECIAL EVENTS

Team members may join organizations voluntarily. Holiday parties and other *NON-RELATED* to work after-work activities are not paid work events.

Employees cannot volunteer away their rights. Events in which the employee's job or the office is improved in some way may not be perceived as "voluntary." All patient-care activities are obviously part of the job and paid. Social activities and other enrichment may not be paid when not work related. If attendance is specifically required by the doctor, the time spent at this activity must always be paid.

Chapter 10

CROSS-TRAINING

I aimed to have the U.S.S. Benfold
four deep in people who
could handle every job onboard.
— Captain D. Michael Abrashoff

One day, you will be without a vital team member in your dental office. Someone will need to step up and fill in. Due to vacation, sickness, or leave, it pays to be constantly prepared for this what-if scenario. Time spent on training backups is time well spent.

Cross-training involves taking the time to train each member of your dental team who already has a primary job to perform all other job functions in the office. Cross-training builds team respect and understanding. It also motivates by building knowledge and new skills. Education in different work areas also prevents workplace boredom. Cross-training provides an internal system of checks and balances, not to mention immediate job replacement. Understanding everyone's job in the dental office challenges each employee; furthermore, it creates appreciation for what each person achieves and contributes to the team.

Besides improving employee and team morale, cross-training will help reduce office HR costs, increase productivity, and reduce turnover. It will allow you to promote from within from a pool of already capable team members and hire new entry-level personnel. It will offer an infinite opportunity for promotion within your organization.

Cross-training demonstrates that the dental office and doctor have faith in each employee's abilities and wants to provide them with the ultimate experience for career growth. In small business, having a highly versatile, well-trained team will help your office remain competitive.

To have a carefully planned and well-organized cross-training program, make a chart of each person and their primary job function. Next, list their immediate replacement in case of illness or vacation. Do this for every member of the office. Have each person train their own replacement. Include employees in this planning process. Go four people deep in the chart-replacement listing. Brainstorm with each team member as to how their job can be improved and how they can get help when help is needed. Adopt the philosophy that we will have many jobs and continue to have "lifelong learning." Cross-training will help you accomplish this goal.

There are tremendous benefits to cross-training. First and foremost, it ensures that you, the practice owner, will never be left empty-handed with a task or a job unfilled because someone is away from the office. Second, cross-training will ensure that an office is not held hostage by a team member who is *the only one* who knows a particular job, system, computer procedure, or, heaven forbid, the password in the office. This serves also as an important safeguard against embezzlement. Third, cross-training builds trust, communication, and appreciation among team members for the particular challenges each person faces in their individual job. This is especially true when it comes to communication and scheduling between the front office and the back office. Clinical dental assistants will appreciate more fully the busy schedule and customer service challenges that team members at the front desk face. Front-desk team members will offer more assistance to back-office clinical assistants once they experience and understand the workload challenges they have with patients within the treatment area.

Once done, post the cross-training schedule on the team bulletin board. Make sure everyone communicates and is fully knowledgeable in all the tasks of the cross-training project. Next time someone is planning to be out for a personal day, make him or her responsible for the planning, skill, proficiency, and performance of their own backup.

Cross-training is a perfect team activity to complete when the doctor is out of the office at a meeting or on vacation. Cross-training is a team-building sport. It's like passing a basketball from person to person, enabling everyone to be able to shoot a basket and score a point. It's very helpful in dissolving misconceptions and barriers between team members. It can also lead to new solutions, initiatives, and efficiencies being created. Best of all, cross-training will relieve the doctor of the stress over a team member's personal days, making them stress free. Cross-training will ensure that the office always runs smoothly.

CASE STUDY 13: "The Neophyte"

Anna was new to the dental office and had been working as a patient coordinator at the front desk for a few months. She was "the Neophyte," the newest member of the team. Soon the office manager and assistant office manager would be gone for an away meeting of the American Association of Dental Office Managers' national convention. Anna was going to be on her own for the very first time.

It would soon be "Showtime!" for Anna. She needed to learn many office functions quickly, including contract preparation, payment posting, deposits, and how to answer questions about insurance. Anna had two weeks of intense cross-training.

The big day came and Anna was "Full steam ahead!" on her own. She did great! Anna was applauded and appreciated. She had grown professionally and had developed new skills in a very short period of time. She had been put to the test and she won! She did it! She had risen to the occasion. Everyone celebrated.

ACTION:

At some point, new team members will need to take over on their own. Dive in and complete cross-training. It will be one of the most rewarding activities your team will experience. Cross-training will produce personal and professional satisfaction, confidence, mutual respect, and ease of everyone involved in the running of a successful dental office.

Chapter 11

ATTENDANCE

No matter how you feel,
get up,
dress up,
show up,
and never give up.
            – Zig Ziglar

Marvelous dental team members "show up" consistently, with enthusiasm and motivation for their dental work. One of the best things about my personal orthodontic team is that they are very, very, very rarely—if ever—out "sick." They rarely miss work due to physical or emotional illness. If they are feeling a bit under the weather, oftentimes they still come in to work and soon find themselves feeling better by the end of the day. If they are infectious or otherwise truly sick, we ask them to please go home.

I'll never forget my first day of restorative class at Harvard School of Dental Medicine. We had a very demanding professor. Her first announcement was "Be here or be dead." This experience and training obviously had an effect on me. I never miss work.

My team also never misses work due to emotional illness, made-up excuses, or just plain apathy. Why is this? The theory may be that the leader is not out "sick." Or, that we do not focus on "sickness" of any kind. We are a healthy group. Health is important to us. We love what we do, and we love being together, serving our patients, working in dentistry and showing up.

The leader leads by example. In my last twenty-five years in practice, I can remember the single day that I was out sick. I had a fever of 103 degrees so I went to the hospital emergency room, where they gave me IV antibiotics and fluid. This episode lasted all night. With no sleep, I figured that I should not go into the office the next day. One day later my fever was completely gone, I felt fine, and I returned to work. Don't expect team members to be any more dedicated to the office than the leader, doctor, office or HR manager.

Knowing that they are missed may help absent individuals come to a fast and immediate recovery. If a team member is out sick, call and ask how they are doing. Wish them, "Get Well Soon!" Let them know that you, the team, and the patients missed them.

In many cultures and parts of the world, illness is just not encouraged. Personally, I come from healthy Polish farm stock. My grandparents, who lived well into their eighties on our family farm, were *never* "sick." All I remember is that they were up at dawn each morning looking forward to the day's chores. I wish the same for all of us. Let's not spotlight and glorify illness in the dental office. There are patients to focus on, and more important things to discuss.

When someone is out unexpectedly, ill or otherwise, we have found that it is not worth bringing in an untrained worker from a temp agency to fill the absence. This could actually produce even more work for the entire dental team and cause more stress, confusion, and inefficiency than being without one team member.

Personal days eliminate surprise absenteeism. Eight weeks' prior notice and written prior approval will guarantee that there will be adequate coverage for the missing team member. An accrued paid vacation day may be used as a personal day. Be generous about personal days. This privilege has never been abused. It has only happened once in 25 years that I asked a team member to reschedule a personal day request (which was coincidentally for a dental appointment!).

Why would you pay someone to be sick? As of July 1, 2015, it is the law in California that all employers must provide all employees with three mandatory sick days annually. Check your state statutes to make sure that your office policy is in compliance with state laws with regards to granting and tracking of "sick days."

The law is the law, and when it comes to HR we need to know it and follow the rules. But let's not encourage sick days. Let's make wellness part of our everyday office culture.

Personal time is important for work/life balance as well as mental and physical health. Take frequent breaks and vacations for the purpose of renewal. This is important to maintaining happiness and a positive life perspective.

Attendance is not only a sign of health and well-being, but it is also a sign of commitment. It is an indication of personal responsibility. It shows dedication. Attendance, after all, is a choice. It is an important decision.

So what happens when you hire someone who is irresponsible, uncommitted, and unmotivated to make it into work? The unexcused absences begin to add up. Here are the most common excuses. Be prepared to hear these and document these and all absences.

1. Death in the Family – Document the name of family member and relationship. When the same family member dies twice with no history of prior illness, it may be time for termination.
2. Doctor's Appointment – Ask for doctor's excuse from treating doctor. Ask that doctor's appointments be prearranged on a non-patient day when possible.
3. Car problems – This problem is up to the employee to solve as quickly as possible. Taxi services are available for emergency transportation.
4. Repeated Family Crises – This could create a chronic problem in attendance and affect the employee's ability to keep their job.
5. "I have cramps" or "I have a headache" – If you have a female dentist as a boss, do not use these excuses. Take medication if necessary or seek medical help.

If you want to improve attendance, keep track of it. Make a chart. Post it on the bulletin board in the team room if necessary. When someone calls in "sick," call and ask them how they are doing. Would they feel well enough to come in by 1:00 p.m.? Many times they will feel better and come into work by the afternoon. They will also appreciate the call if they are truly sick. They feel loved and important, and many times this in itself makes them feel better.

The absent are never without fault,
nor the present without excuse.
– Benjamin Franklin

CASE STUDY 14: "THE FREQUENTLY MISSING"

Being absent is a big deal. It is not so easy to forget. I once gave a lecture at a nearby dental school. All of the students and assistants of the department were present. The topic of absenteeism was discussed. I *randomly* asked a young woman sitting in the front row, "How many days were *you* out last year?" The young woman looked flustered. She squirmed in her chair but remained silent. I was perplexed. How could someone not remember the ballpark figure of how many days they missed work the previous year?

There are many things that can keep a person from work other than uncontrollable illness. One possibility is drug and alcohol abuse. This problem most commonly surfaces on Monday mornings after a long weekend. Beware of Monday morning absenteeism or the Sunday night phone calls from employee family members. Worse yet is being AWOL (Absent Without Leave) on Monday. These could be signs of a seriously destructive lifestyle.

I continued on with my lecture. It turned out that the person whom I randomly asked about absenteeism was chronically absent. This had been a big problem for the department. Here lies the problem.

ACTION:

Address the problem of absenteeism! If there is a real problem, it needs attention. Certainly, it is interfering with the normal day-to-day life of this individual and their ability to perform a job function. Addressing absenteeism seriously is the first step to its elimination. Otherwise, you are enabling undesirable and dysfunctional organizational and personal work behavior.

Hard work spotlights the character of people:
some turn up their sleeves,
some turn up their noses,
and some don't turn up at all.
– Sam Ewing

Absence is a sign to consider. It can indicate a lack of team participation and motivation. Absenteeism at fun office events (though voluntary, and not controllable by the HR manager) is a serious sign that this person is not committed to her fellow team members, her doctor, her office, her patients, and ultimately her job. This individual has no personal connection or emotional attachment to the office family. They just don't care. Most likely, they will soon leave the office of their own volition. They've already got "one foot out the door."

Lack of volunteer participation is a sign of disinterest or apathy. This person may already be looking for another job. They have no reason to give any extra effort or time to the doctor, office, or the team. They may even be planning to leave dentistry altogether.

CASE STUDY 15: "The Mercenary"

It was time for the annual Patient Appreciation Party at the local bowling alley. The associate doctor Sonja asked, "Will I be paid to attend the annual party?" The answer was "No."

ACTION:

No one in the dental office, including the doctor who owns the practice gets paid to attend a patient appreciation party on a Saturday night. It is totally voluntary and optional. This activity is in appreciation of patients to thank them for choosing our dental office and paying our salaries.

Most people are happy to show up and share the love at a social event. If you have to be paid to have fun, then perhaps you're in the wrong field in the wrong place. Appreciate that you have a job and patients to serve.

When it comes to volunteerism, all stakeholders in the practice should feel some ownership for the events which they provide. By not attending, they will be missed. Enthusiasm is important. Consistency of attendance is a tremendous benefit to the community, patients, doctor, and the entire team. Everyone loves someone they can count on. Everyone counts and every moment counts.

Chapter 12

LEAVE

You can decorate absence however you want—
but you're still going to feel what's missing."
– Siobhan Vivian

Leave policies are largely based on laws that exist at the federal and state level. As the largest-population state in the union, with more than 10% of the country's populace, California is often a model for other states. "As California goes, so goes the nation."

Since California is a very liberal state, you can be assured that if you design your practice in keeping with the following guidelines, you will probably be acting in accord with the laws in your state. But, to be certain, please check with your local HR attorney or HR advisor.

There are several types of leave required by law. In the state of California these include:

1. Family leave
2. Sick leave (California)
3. Jury duty
4. Emergency duty as a volunteer firefighter, reserve police officer, or emergency rescue personnel
5. Time off to visit the school of a child
6. Time off to appear at school when required by the school
7. Time off to vote

8. Drug and/or alcohol rehabilitation
9. Literacy assistance
10. Temporary military leave and/or reserve duty

MEDICAL LEAVE

Any regular full-time team member who is temporarily unable to work due to a medical condition will be granted a leave of absence for the period of their illness. The reasons for medical leave include pregnancy, childbirth, and other severe medical conditions.

A physician's note must be provided to verify the beginning and expected ending dates of medical leave. After using all sick days, team members must take any available vacation days and pay as part of the approved medical leave. State Disability Insurance (SDI) may then be used to extend medical leave once sick days and vacation pay have been used.

If a team member sustains a work-related injury or illness, they are eligible for a medical leave of absence for the period of disability in accordance with all applicable laws covering occupational disabilities (Workers' Compensation Policy).

Benefits and vacation-day accrual do not apply during approved medical leave. Accepting other employment or filing for Unemployment Insurance benefits while on medical leave may be treated as a voluntary resignation from employment.

Once the period of medical or disability leave has exceeded four weeks in a 12-month period, you may hire a temporary replacement.

Once on medical leave or disability leave, prior to returning to their position, the team member must provide a written release from their medical doctor. Should abilities change upon return of the team member, a reasonable effort must be made to reintegrate the team member to their original position. The office cannot guarantee reinstatement in the same position as arrangements may have been made for additional training of other team members or new hires in the team member's absence. Team assignments or the economic environment may have changed during a team member's absence. If a team member fails to return to work promptly at the end of their medical leave, this may be accepted as a form a resignation as stated in the Team Member Handbook.

CASE STUDY 16: "The Stranger"

Anita had a stroke. In her sixties, she had been a devoted employee for thirty-five years. She was valued and loved by the doctor and the team. Everyone waited with anticipation for Anita's return to work.

Anita finally returned to the office after one year of medical leave. It was as if she were a different person. This was not the Anita that everyone knew and had worked with so well. This was a stranger. Interactions with Anita were not smooth. Her new level of work was accommodated as much as possible for her disability. Her actions and performance deviations were documented.

Events culminated one day when Anita called a patient an unfavorable name in Portuguese. The patient, who also spoke Portuguese, reported this unprofessional behavior in a complaint to the doctor. The doctor quickly spoke with Anita regarding the incident. Anita exclaimed aloud in front of all present "I Quit!" The doctor requested this statement in writing. Anita refused and stormed out of the office. Witnesses wrote a description of the events and signed a written statement. The doctor also signed this history and placed it in Anita's personnel file. A severance check, including accrued vacation pay, was issued to Anita within 72 hours.

Anita tried to sue the doctor for age discrimination. There was no basis for the action, and the case was dismissed.

ACTION:

Medical leaves are difficult for everyone involved, especially for those who are medically compromised. These situations need to be handled carefully with empathy, understanding, candor, and documentation. When possible, accommodations need to be made. Whenever terminating after return from a protected leave, you will have to prove that separation was for a legitimate reason, non-discriminatory, based on unacceptable performance, and unrelated to the protected leave.

Family Leave

The California Family Right Act (CFRA) is for employers with fifty (50) or more part-time or full-time employees. To be eligible for CFRA, an employee must have more than 12 months of service with the employer and have worked at least 1,250 hours. Employees may take unpaid time off to care for a seriously ill parent, spouse or child, for the employee's own serious health condition or to bond with an adopted or foster child. Since most dental offices are less than fifty (50) employees, this law would apply only to large corporate dental chains.

PREGNANCY LEAVE

In the state of California, employers in dental offices with five or more persons have an obligation pertaining to Pregnancy Disability Leave (PDL). An employee is entitled to take up to four months of unpaid disability leave before or after giving birth when unable to work because of pregnancy or a pregnancy-related condition.

Team members often take one month off prior to delivery and three months off after delivery. Employees are not required to take the full four months, and they may return when ready with a doctor's note. A written request of the date of pregnancy leave is best given to the dental office a minimum of one month ahead of the start of leave. The anticipated date of return for pregnancy leave should also be stated, as this will be helpful to the office in the adjustment of schedules or temporary hire of additional help.

Many disability policies purchased by doctors cover pregnancy leave and will provide payment for lost income during time off for pregnancy.

It is possible that special arrangements or reduced hours may be scheduled for dental team members during pregnancy. Whenever arrangements are made for pregnancy leave, *be sure to have everything documented in writing and signed by both parties.*

Accrued vacation pay and sick days may also be used at the time of pregnancy leave. After this has been used to completion, the pregnancy leave team member may collect SDI, which will provide partial salary continuation after a designated waiting period.

PAID FAMILY LEAVE

Paid family leave usually applies to companies with fifty (50) or more employees. All California workers contribute to a pool of funds that has been set aside to pay for Paid Family Leave. These funds are collected every payroll period through the SDI deduction. Paid Family Leave is funded entirely by team member contributions.

The Paid family leave program provides a maximum of six weeks of paid time off within a 12-month period for team members to care for a child, spouse, parent or domestic partner with a serious health condition or to bond with a newborn or foster child. This time may be taken all at once or on an intermittent basis.

For more information on Family Leave, contact the Department of Fair Employment and Housing (DFEH) in your state or visit their website. In California, this can be found at www.dfeh.ca.gov. More information in California on paid leave under Family Temporary Disability Insurance (FTDI) administered by the Employment Development Department (EDD) can be found at www.edd.ca.gov.

Sick Leave

An employer who provides sick leave must permit an employee to use accrued sick leave to attend to a child, parent or spouse who is ill. In the state of California as of July 1, 2015, each employee must have three days paid sick leave per year for their own use. For more information on sick days, contact an HR professional in your area.

Jury Duty

Jury duty is a civic responsibility of all U.S. citizens including the team members and the doctor. It is not a requirement to compensate employees for time off to serve on juries or to appear as a witness. Vacation pay may be used for jury duty.

Jury duty, however, is a hardship for the dental office in terms of scheduling and workload redistribution when someone is missing. Most dentists work with small teams. The employee must give reasonable notice to the employer when leaving for jury duty so that accommodations can be made.

Encourage team members to list available dates for jury duty during times when the dental office is closed as alternatives for fulfilling their obligation. Christmas, New Year's and Thanksgiving weeks are very good times of year to enter as a preference for jury duty as is a week when the office is closed for vacation.

An employee must also be given time off to appear in court when they are a victim of a crime or required to appear as a witness. For instance, an employer may not discriminate against an employee for taking time off to obtain relief as a result of domestic violence.

EMERGENCY DUTY AS A VOLUNTEER FIREFIGHTER, RESERVE POLICE OFFICER, OR EMERGENCY RESCUE PERSONNEL

An employer in the state of California must provide leaves of absence for employees required to perform emergency duty as a volunteer firefighter, a reserve police officer, or as emergency rescue personnel. The employee is not compensated during this time off.

TIME OFF TO VISIT THE SCHOOL OF A CHILD

In the state of California, employers with twenty-five or more employees working at one location must allow a parent, grandparent, or guardian up to forty hours off per year to participate in activities at his or her child's school, including a day care facility. The employee must give reasonable notice to the employer. Employees must first utilize vacation days. This time off to visit the school is not compensated.

TIME OFF TO APPEAR AT SCHOOL WHEN REQUIRED BY THE SCHOOL

All employers in the state of California must allow a parent, grandparent or guardian of a student to appear at the school when the school has given advanced notice of this request. Should the child of a team member have problems at school related to suspension or disciplinary action, the team member may need to leave work temporarily. Vacation pay may be used for this lost time. The employee is required to give reasonable notice to the employer.

TIME OFF TO VOTE

Team members are encouraged to fulfill their civic responsibilities by participating and voting in elections. Team members are encouraged to vote before work on Election Day or earlier by absentee ballot. In the state of California, when needed, the office will grant up to two hours of paid time off to vote. Team members must submit a voter's receipt on the first working day following the election to qualify for up to two hours off to vote on Election Day.

Drug and/or Alcohol Rehabilitation

In the state of California, employers with twenty-five or more employees must reasonably accommodate an employee's voluntary participation in an alcohol and/or drug rehabilitation program. The employer must also make a reasonable effort to safeguard an employee's privacy with regard to his or her enrollment in a rehabilitation program. An employer may refuse to hire or can discharge an employee because of the employee's current use of alcohol and/or drugs, or because the employee is unable to perform his or her duties.

Literacy Assistance

Employers with twenty-five or more employees in the state of California must reasonably accommodate and assist any employee who reveals a literacy problem and requests employer assistance either in enrolling in a literacy program or in arranging visits of an instructor to the job site, provided that such accommodation does not impose hardship on the employer.

Temporary Military Leave and/or Reserve Duty

Military leave of absence will be granted to a team member who is a member of the Reserved Corps of the Armed Forces of the United States, the National Guard, or the National Militia to attend drills, training, or active duty with the U.S. Armed Services. Military leave is unpaid. Team members may use vacation pay during these times.

If a team member is called for service of more than 30 days but less than 181 days, they may apply for re-employment within 14 days after release from military duty in accordance with all applicable state and federal laws.

It will be up to the employer what additional leaves they will want to include in the Team Handbook. The Team Handbook must be tailored to all applicable federal, state, county, and municipal laws and regulations, according to the number of employees in your business and further modified by office culture and personal requests. In many circumstances, it will be up to the practice owner when and how accrued vacation pay can be used with many personal leaves that fall outside of statutory regulations. For assistance with leaves and the construction of your Team Handbook, contact an HR professional.

Part Four

BEHAVIORS

Behaviors are a choice.
Feelings are sometimes out of our control.
Behavior has to do with choices.
– Randall Terry

A s employers, it's important that dentists feel confident that each team member is dedicated to the office, patients, and the team. This sentiment either grows or diminishes over time, based on the concrete actions and performance of the individual. The employer must be able to assess work performance outcomes objectively. To do this, one must have a baseline standard of desirable and undesirable work behaviors.

Here is an important HR litmus test to remember: *when a person with desirable work behaviors is absent, they are missed; when someone has undesirable work behaviors, it is often a welcomed holiday when that team member is away.* Negative employees also affect the bottom line. They bring everyone in the dental office down, including patients. In the end, they diminish cash flow and revenue. *In the end, the bottom line is the collective outcome of employee performance in the dental office.*

I once read an interesting business book written by Donald Keough, the CEO of Coca Cola Company. In it, Mr. Keough described why businesses fail; he gave many important life and business lessons taken from his own experience. One lesson described what his father had taught him at a young age on how to inspect bulls for purchase at the cattle yard in Sioux City, South Dakota. His father warned, "Don't get wrapped up with the person selling the bull. He will catch your attention and pull you into liking him in an effort to get you to favorably like his bull. *To be objective, keep your eye on the bull."*

I've often thought of this advice when thinking of underperforming or undesirable team members. They pull the doctor and teammates into their personalities and their personal lives at which point we do not accurately assess their performance. After a while, we establish a relationship with them and we may even start feeling sorry for them. It is a challenge of HRM in small business and dental offices to make objective, direct HR decisions based solely on performance and the best interests of the business. Yet, this is exactly what we must do. Remember to *"Keep your eye on performance, not the person."*

Chapter 13

DESIRABLE WORK BEHAVIORS

In all forms of leadership,
whether you are a coach, a CEO, or a parent,
there are four words that when said,
can bring out the best in your team, your employees, and your family.
I BELIEVE IN YOU.
– Coach K.

When we find an ideal employee, someone who adds to the team and makes the dental office workforce stronger and the office more productive, life is good. Everyone is happy with someone with a smile on his or her face, who is joyful, and just great to be around. It makes work wonderful. It makes the office fun. It makes every workday a blessing.

Ideal work behaviors are the HR management gold standard. In order to instill these qualities in your office personnel, it is important that these qualities be rewarded. Individuals who exhibit and possess these behaviors are keepers.

DESIRABLE WORK BEHAVIORS
1. Filling in for others
2. Volunteering
3. Taking initiative

4. Helping others
5. Assisting the doctor
6. Improving the dental practice
7. Punctuality
8. Attendance

The fulfillment of these good behaviors requires discipline and emotional intelligence. Positive team members with great attitudes volunteer, take initiative, and happily share the workload. They are self-motivated. Not only are they awesome teammates, but they also help the doctor and make great suggestions to continually improve the dental office. They are focused on serving the patient. They are punctual and have excellent attendance. They have earned the trust and respect of the patients, the team, and the doctor.

CASE STUDY 17: "THE PERFORMER"

Carolyn had worked in dentistry for her entire life. At age fifty-four, she was a front-office greeter, concierge, patient coordinator, and manager of all aspects of the dental office. She was the first full-time, long-time employee that the doctor had hired. She was professional and courteous at all times. Her appearance was always attractive. She was happily married for over twenty-five years and the mother of two high school students. She used pleasant language and proper English, always saying, "Please," "Thank you," and "You're Welcome." She even spoke up to correct the doctor's grammar and English.

Carolyn's desk was always well organized. She was committed and seldom out "sick." She got along with all team members and she was not afraid to speak up when someone was out of line. She played the role of office mother. The doctor himself considered Carolyn a trusted confidant. Carolyn was a high performer. She did everything well.

Carolyn had good work-life balance. As a wife and mother, she always gave her family top priority; she was organized enough to give the office six weeks' notice if she needed time for personal affairs or vacations.

Carolyn finally left the dental office when her children were in high school. She wanted the summers off to be with her children before they left for college. She applied for a job with the public school system, which had better family work hours and benefits. The doctor gave Carolyn an excellent work reference. She gave the office advance notice before leaving so that she could train the new person as her replacement.

Carolyn was a high-functioning professional. She was always missed by the office after she left. She created the highest standard possible and she could not be replaced.

ACTION:

For someone as good as Carolyn, *"break all the rules."* Excellent team members are hard to find. They do exist. When you find one, hold on to them for as long as you can. Give them the summers off if need be. Make sure they know how much they are appreciated.

Part Five

UNDESIRABLE WORK BEHAVIORS

Deliver us from evil.
> – The Lord's Prayer

Aesop wrote a fable entitled, "The Frog and the Scorpion." It goes like this:

There was a Frog and a Scorpion. One day, the Scorpion asked the Frog, "May I have a ride across the pond on your back?"

The Frog replied, "That would be very foolish of me to give you a ride across the pond. You have a deadly stinger. It is highly likely you will sting me, and I will die."

The Scorpion argued, "Why would I sting you? That would be very foolish of me. If I were to use my deadly stinger on you, you would die, I would fall into the pond, and we would both die by drowning in the pond. It does not make good sense for me to do that!"

The Frog reasoned, "That's true, your logic is persuasive. Even though you have a stinger and your sting is lethal, it does not make sense for you to sting me. You also seem nice, you look good, your talk is sweet, and you want to be my friend. This all appears and sounds very good to me."

And so, the Frog agreed to give the Scorpion a ride across the pond. The Scorpion cheerfully climbed onto Frog's back. Then, in the middle of the pond, the Scorpion stung the Frog. Mortally wounded, the Frog cried out "Why did you do that? Now we will both die!" The Scorpion answered, *"Because, it's in my nature."*

This is often the scenario in a dental office. The frog is the dentist, Dr. Nice Guy or Dr. Angel Gal. The scorpion is the new employee with a unique destructive nature to which they are true and cannot control. With an undesirable-behavior employee, exorbitant amounts of time, money, and attention are given in an effort to remold their unacceptable inclinations. *What great HR managers know is that not everyone has unlimited potential.* Seasoned HR professionals avoid hiring a scorpion in the first place.

Undesirable work behaviors are perhaps the most important topic in HR management. What we can learn from fairytales and history is that there is often a villain: someone who does harm, complicates the situation, and prevents everyone from living in peace and harmony. Undesirable Work Behaviors is a difficult and unpopular topic to discuss. No one wants to be perceived as a "bad guy." Hence, the research and information available on undesirable work behaviors is often neglected, or swept under the rug.

In this world of political correctness and employment lawsuits, managers and leaders may feel afraid to speak up and take action about an underlying negative situation caused by a specific individual in the dental office. *Although hard to accept, addressing undesirable issues is exactly what needs to be done.*

Every person comes with a variety of traits, personalities, and peculiarities. When problems arise, it is important to identify and address them immediately or soon after they occur. Once addressed, one must ask, "With this problem, can this individual continue to work here as a valued and contributing member of the team?"

If you experience negative actions such as the inability to follow through on tasks, absenteeism, argumentativeness, or frank insubordination, this will immediately diminish confidence in that team member and also you as the HR manager or leader. In the long run, trust will be diminished or lost. Once trust is lacking in a team member, you have the choice of continuing to work with this individual in a handicapped manner, practicing *"snoopervision,"* or cutting your losses and moving on to rebuild your dream team.

Our HR goal in dentistry is to spend time doing what we love, practicing dentistry in an environment in which we are comfortable, with people we enjoy. Each of us wants to work with positive, supportive, competent people. Yet, it is rare to have a dental office team that is perfect in every way.

Negative experiences can be brought home from the dental office, affecting family time. It's a gnawing feeling when you realize that someone at work is negative, unsupportive, incompetent, or psychologically disturbed. Undesirable work behaviors pull down morale and also the quality of dental office life. Left unresolved, this environment can even keep you up at night.

The first step in eliminating undesirable work behaviors is to clearly identify that they exist and to understand them.

Undesirable Work Behaviors
1. Taking company equipment or proceeds
2. Exaggerated work hours
3. Intentionally working slowly or not at all
4. Staying out of sight to avoid work
5. Gossiping about co-workers
6. Starting negative rumors
7. Covering up mistakes
8. Competing with team members
9. Blaming others for their personal mistakes

The list of antisocial, deviant and destructive workplace behaviors is long. In some institutions, the term "Counterproductive Work Behaviors" (CWB) is often used to describe negative and undesirable acts in the workplace.

"Misbehaviors" at work are common. It is not necessary to write an incident report every time one team member annoys someone or creates a small problem. Sometimes, simply saying, "Snap out of it!" or "Let's do it differently next time," will suffice. It is, however, necessary to take action for repeated offenses or undesirable behavior which creates chronic team conflict and diminishes office performance. It is easy to say, "Turn that frown upside down," but can we recognize when a bad attitude in ingrained in the individual?

Stopping undesirable workplace behaviors will not be easy. Not every situation can be rehabilitated. Once you have documented the facts, make it a habit to talk with the team member in question as soon as possible. Rather than letting undesirable work behaviors fester and grow for years until there is a major blow-up, aim to "nip the problem in the bud." Deal with issues as soon as possible.

Precisely explain your concerns to an employee with an undesirable workplace behavior and point out the consequences of this behavior. Demonstrate how their action reduces their performance and harms the dental office, your team, and ultimately your patients. Document this conversation. Soon, your dental office will run more smoothly and be a happier and more successful work environment. You will feel a sense of peace for doing so.

Many dental consultants are accused by dentists of "Cinderella-ism." Wave a magic wand, mutter a few incantations, make a wish, spend a day with me, and all of your HR problems will be gone. You and your team may feel temporarily better, in a psychological state of euphoria. But *action* is what is required to change an undesirable situation. *Action is needed to achieve permanent change.* Education is great, but without implementation nothing changes. A consultant may not do the implementation for you. You must, with courage, communication, and candor, do it yourself.

"Peter Pan" may describe a coach who flies in and flies out, superficially assessing a very difficult, recalcitrant situation. The determination might be, "Doctor, the problem is you!" No resolution to the problem is prescribed, and the assessor flies off several thousands of dollars richer to the next dental office visit. A dentist friend once spent $50,000 for a one-year minimum contract of consulting with a dental office management "expert." His practice numbers were reviewed and he was told that his HR overhead was too high, alone over 40% of collections. Logically, he needed to cut back hours or lay off a few people. But he couldn't do it. And, even after spending tens of thousands of dollars nothing changed; nothing changed at all.

Leadership is change. Leadership takes courage, communication, and candor. *Dentists are often too nice.* They have a difficult time making logical business decisions or being totally honest when giving reviews. As healthcare givers, we avoid being uncomfortable or hurting the feelings of another. In this way when it comes to HR management, dentists may suffer at their own peril.

Authors and consultants prefer to stay positive and upbeat. They want to be loved by their clients. Who wouldn't? As an orthodontist with twenty-five years of in-office practical experience, I am free to write of scenarios I have seen, experienced, or which have been shared with me by dentists, consultants, advisors, and other colleagues in the real world of dental practice management, without personal ramifications. HR situations are not always ideal. They are certainly not fun to deal with or maybe even read about. They are, however, the reality of HR management life.

Undesirable work behaviors fall into three general categories: embezzlement, poor work ethic, and dysfunctional behaviors. We will begin with embezzlement. This may be the most frequent, the most problematic, and the most damaging of all undesirable workplace behaviors.

Chapter 14

EMBEZZLEMENT

Corruption, embezzlement, fraud,
these are all characteristics which exist everywhere.
It is regrettably the way human nature functions,
whether we like it or not.
What successful economies do is keep it to a minimum.
No one has ever eliminated any of that stuff.
— Alan Greenspan

Published statistics, including some from the ADA and from Dumoulin and Associates, suggest that between 50 to 60% of dentists will be embezzled. The true number is probably much higher, because some embezzlement is never detected, and other embezzlement is found by the doctor but no action is taken. It is impossible to know the exact magnitude of embezzlement in dentistry, but we do know that the incidence is shockingly high.

One of the mistakes that many dentists make with embezzlement is that they assume that it is possible to discourage embezzlers by "denial of opportunity" strategies—essentially trying to "lock down" pathways that an embezzler might use to steal. While this "hard target" approach might work well for other types of crime (such as putting an alarm on your house to prevent robbery), it is unlikely to prevent embezzlement in the dental office. Distinct from other types of economic crime, in dental embezzlement, the victim is preordained. The victim is you, the owner of the dental office. It is just a matter of which option, from hundreds of choices, the villain will use to embezzle from you.

As in any crime, there needs to be motive and opportunity. While it is possible to deny *some* opportunity, a *complete* denial of opportunity in the dental office is difficult. The thief will already be working in your office. There will be too many opportunities open to be able to shut them all down. Therefore, being able to screen out potential embezzlers when hiring, and being able to spot the telltale clues that embezzlement is happening, or is about to happen, are the best strategies to combat embezzlement.

> *An ounce of prevention is worth*
> *a pound of cure.*
> – Benjamin Franklin

The psychological theories to explain why one becomes a thief are many fold. There could be financial needs secondary to personal issues such as drug addiction, gambling, family illness, or an expensive divorce. There could be a deviant personality disorder, which rationalizes stealing or steals for the thrill of doing so. There could be excessive greed. There may be moral laxity without ethical standards or trustworthiness. Or finally, there can be low social standing in marginal individuals who steal as a way of expressing grievances with the office or with their life situation.

Sometimes embezzlement is of a petty nature and may involve things such as paper clips, pens, paper, and pencils. The thief may also take items such as postage stamps, light bulbs, toilet paper, batteries or other office supplies. While it is tempting to dismiss these thefts as "insignificant," they make a statement about the character of the person doing the stealing and their lack of respect for your property.

> *There are not small frauds;*
> *just large frauds that are caught early.*
> – W. Steve Albrecht PhD, CFE, CPA
> Legendary fraud investigator

Theft requires motivation, opportunity and rationalization. Petty thieves have already displayed that all three ingredients are present for them; therefore the progression from small to large-scale stealing for them is a very easy one. Therefore, petty thievery should result in dismissal, and this message should be clearly conveyed to new and existing employees.

The activities of the thief can also be broad and bold in scope. The thief may take expensive items such as cameras and computer equipment. Items may suddenly disappear from the dental office. Missing items may sometimes be mysteriously found in the thief's possession, at their home, or on eBay.

The most appealing target in the dental practice for the thief is money. Although many practitioners focus on the theft of cash, there are many additional options for an enterprising embezzler to steal wealth from a practice. For example, personal expenses of the thief could end up being charged to the doctor's credit card. Cash, checks, and credit card payments made to the practice by patients or insurance companies could end up being waylaid and monetized by the thief. The dentist's payroll records also could be tampered with and "creative accounting" done to abuse bonus programs that the office has in place to falsely overpay employees.

Embezzlers can also steal and sell information of various types, or they can use the office's resources to improperly obtain narcotics for personal use or resale. It has even been reported that dental staff with some level of clinical training have performed dental procedures on people after hours, using the dentist's supplies and equipment, and charging fraudulently for their services. This is the most shocking of all forms of "indirect" embezzlement because it deprives the dentist of revenue, and it poses a considerable danger to the practice's reputation and the patient's health.

Embezzlement is broad in scope and limitless. Although dental office theft is a common crime, it is extremely difficult to prosecute. Many dentists do not make complaints to the police. Police reports of embezzlement go to the District Attorney's office. The DA's office usually has many cases deemed more important than dental embezzlement, like child abuse and murder. "Petty" white-collar crime is not a threat to public safety. In addition, the victim, the dentist, is often not terribly motivated for prosecution. Lastly, the victim would be considered by most to be a privileged member of society and therefore not at the top of the District Attorney's office list of victims in need of urgent justice.

David Harris is CEO of Prosperident, a firm that specializes in dental embezzlement. He is a Private Investigator and a Certified Fraud Examiner. He is also certified in Financial Forensics. David Harris reports, "The *average* dental embezzlement we see is over $100,000 and we have seen more than a couple of cases where over a million dollars was embezzled from a dental practice. Embezzlement is a large-scale problem in dentistry."

> *White-collar crime gets more outrageous*
> *by the second in America.*
> – Sara Paretsky

CASE STUDY 18: "The Techie"

The IT charges at the local dental society seemed a bit high. The new president of the organization decided that he would like to see the computer items charged on the society's credit card by the local dental society director, Tom. However, the newly charged electronics could not be found at the office.

The president decided that he would speak with the District Attorney regarding the possibility of embezzlement. The District Attorney said that he felt that he had enough evidence to hold a raid of Tom's home. There, the dental society's computer equipment was indeed found. The executive director of the local dental society had been selling the society's equipment on eBay!

ACTION:

Total elimination of embezzlement is an impossible task. To stop embezzlement, you would have to eliminate the *desire* to steal. This is an impossible task, because we are dentists and healthcare professionals, not psychologists, psychiatrists, or police officers. Accordingly, we must do our best to recognize the signs of embezzlement in an effort to limit the possible damage from this behavior.

The best defense against theft is constant warning and surveillance. The misbehavior of theft *CANNOT* be rehabilitated, and a staff member who steals, no matter how small the amount, should be terminated, regardless of how difficult they might be to replace or how valuable they might otherwise be to the practice.

Embezzlement expert David Harris of Prosperident tells me that while he doesn't believe that anything can be done to *prevent* embezzlement, he thinks that there are many things that a doctor can do to increase the probability of detection and minimize damage from embezzlement. Some of David's suggestions include:

Behave ethically. Dentists cutting ethical corners (such as failing to collect insurance co-pays or pocketing cash receipts without reporting them as income) are effectively handing embezzlers a "get out of jail free" card.

Make proper use of security features in practice management software. Everyone needs their own user ID and password, and "authority" levels need to be properly established in the software so that staff can do their jobs, but are not granted access to some functions (such as adjustments and write-offs) that could allow embezzlement to be concealed.

Have an alarm system for the office, and monitor access by staff after-hours. Most thieves like "alone-time" in the office, and you need to know if someone is there after-hours.

Do not allow staff to have remote access to the practice management software. Monitoring usage is difficult. Do not allow team members to have computer access from home or other locations. Removing this will allow your alarm system to monitor extra-curricular activity.

*Make it an office policy that every staff member take a vacation of at least two weeks per year **when the office is open,** and do not allow their work to be "held over" until their return.* This forces a level of cross-training in the office that has other benefits, and having someone else performing an embezzler's work while he or she is away provides an excellent opportunity for detection.

There are well-known warning signs associated with embezzlement. One characteristic sign of embezzlement is an employee offering to work during vacations and after hours. Refusing to share duties at the front desk is also worrisome. Another concern is replying to questions with nervous and unreasonable explanations, especially when it comes to low collections. The embezzler gets annoyed and agitated at reasonable questions regarding collections. They will retaliate with pronounced criticism, focusing on others in an effort to divert suspicion from themselves.

Excessive friendliness with the dental-practice owner could also be a sign of cover-up. Something that may surprise a lot of practice owners is that the majority of embezzlement discovery is prompted by behavioral changes as opposed to financial irregularities. Be aware of these subtle signs. Also be aware that embezzlement may occur by a long-term trusted team member, with five or more years of tenure, who may have had a personal setback or psychological change of mind.

A thief believes everybody steals.
– E. W. Howe

CASE STUDY 19: "THE WHITE-COLLAR CRIMINAL"

Maria was employed as a treatment coordinator in a large dental group practice. With curly blonde hair and blue eyes, she wore a pretty flowered dress with a white lace collar to her initial interview. She stated that she was a wife and mother. She was very involved in her church. She was new to the area. She was an attractive woman, slim, physically fit, and over the age of 40. She was a homeowner and her husband had a good job as a manager of a local retail store.

After a few months, the doctor noticed that collections were unusually low. He asked Maria why patients hadn't paid. Maria became outspokenly annoyed and barked back at this reasonable inquiry. She stated that when the doctor was on vacation, patients didn't pay.

The doctor went home and checked the production and collection records for the previous months. He compared that month to the same month in the previous year. He knew something was wrong. After Maria had left work the next day, the doctor and the office manager pulled the charts of the last 10 new patients to check the contracts and down payments recorded. They quickly noticed that every new contract had an unexplained down payment write-off.

Nothing was said to Maria regarding the evidence that had been found or that she was suspected of embezzlement. *Nothing was said to her about the write-offs or possible embezzlement.* The next day Maria was reassigned to a new position at the front desk and relieved of all contract entry and money-collection duties. Through luck, rather than planning, the next day, Maria voluntarily quit.

The following month, several patients commented that their initial cash down payment was not reflected in the balance of their account history. These patients were asked to bring in their down-payment receipts. What they brought to the office were handwritten receipts on paper taken from a receipt pad purchased at the local office supply store, not the computer-generated receipt from the office computer system as customarily given. These patients stated that Maria had told them that the initial down payment needed to be made in cash.

Maria was the only person in charge of these down payments in this practice. The police were called and an incident report was filed with the District Attorney. The District Attorney was given the handwritten receipts as well as the patients' names and phone numbers as evidence. It was estimated that Maria had stolen at least $40,000 over two to three months' time.

An investigation by the police revealed that this was the third charge filed against Maria for embezzlement. Her first incident occurred when she was a teen; she had stolen her grandmother's Social Security checks. Her second crime was at her last place of employment, another small business. This was her third case of embezzlement. If Maria were convicted of a third strike in the state of California, she would go to jail.

What was also revealed by the investigation was that Maria was on her third marriage. She had six children, for none of which she had custody. She had been married for a short time to her present husband. She had opened a separate bank account. Cash deposits had been made to that account. Her husband called the doctor one evening crying regarding the investigation. The doctor told the husband to have Maria return the money. Maria never did.

As the investigation dragged on, Maria applied for a job in another dental office. The new office doctor called for a reference for Maria. The doctor was told, "*Under NO circumstances, would we EVER rehire this former employee.*" The new dental office called for a second time. Again, the new dental office was warned, "*NEVER, under any circumstance would our office EVER rehire this former employee.*" The new dental office hired Maria anyway. Within one month, she embezzled from her new office.

The District Attorney's office put Maria's case into a large stack of cases. They told the dental office that they would get to Maria's case as soon as they could, if at all, since white-collar crime was not at the top of their priority list. They had drug dealers and child molesters to prosecute. The dental office never heard from the District Attorney's office again. When last heard from, Maria was still seeking employment in a dental office.

ACTION:

There are many lessons to be learned from this case study. First, to allow this person to remain in the practice for even another day in ANY capacity was a high-risk exercise. Had this person not quit, she would have found another way to steal. Yet, even when presented with the evidence, practice owners may still be unbelieving that embezzlement has taken place. This is the wrong way to deal with embezzlement. Accept it. It is a shockingly irrational action in an otherwise rational world. Deal with embezzlement quickly. Remove the embezzler immediately.

Second, it was erroneous for the practice owner to assume that if opportunity were removed, stealing wouldn't happen. Statistics describing embezzlement reveal that embezzlers will find another way to steal. Never underestimate the determination and creativity of the Thief.

Third, dentists may be reluctant or embarrassed to exert pressure on the DA to follow through on an embezzlement case. It is our moral duty to apprehend criminals and protect fellow dentists from embezzlement. Never give up.

Fourth, this case illustrated the importance of background checks. Maria is an example of a "serial embezzler" who has stolen in the past, and so she can reasonably be expected to embezzle again from future employers. *Do thorough background checks on all potential hires.* Call the last employer (obtaining the phone number independently from an online search engine—do not call any phone number given to you by an applicant). Ask if they would rehire. If they say "NO," believe them! Ask if there is any reason to check public records.

Beware of drifters, people who are marginal with no tenure or community social standing. They have no history of ever having developed commitment, which is often the background of those who steal.

While the serial embezzlers grab people's attention and make for interesting conversation, the vast majority of dollars embezzled from dentists are taken by long-term employees with no criminal past. David Harris of Prosperident tells me that less than 15% of his company's cases involve serial embezzlers. There are many reasons why long-term employees may suddenly start stealing. Sometimes they have undergone a devastating life change, or event. Examples include divorce, a child on drugs, or a gambling problem. Whatever the reason, they use their intimate knowledge of the systems in place, and the trust that they have accumulated over their employment to devastating effect. They avoid the mistakes that may trip up serial embezzlers, allowing the long-term employee to steal more, and get away with it for far longer. Watch for troubling changes in behavior and unusual reactions, especially when asked about money.

Embezzlers, in particular, masquerade as ideal employees. Many dentists have a utopian vision of the "practice that runs itself," freeing them to deliver excellent clinical dentistry. Thieves recognize this fault, and play to it. Embezzlers often present themselves as highly efficient, organized and hard-working employees, which earns them your misplaced trust. They may be overly friendly. They may even invite the doctor over for dinner or volunteer at out-of- office events. They also convince the doctor to short-circuit or ignore steps and evidence presented during normal business procedures.

Should you receive a defensive response surrounding questions regarding collections, probe deeply. An ADA survey released in 2008 examined how victims realized that they had been embezzled. More than two-thirds indicated that it was a behavioral anomaly rather than a financial irregularity that led them to believe that theft was occurring. These behavioral abnormalities may include not wanting to take vacation, being unwilling to cross-train another team member, or resisting involvement with outside advisors, consultants, or software trainers. Be on the lookout and note these warning behaviors.

The world does not need another credit card.
– Suze Orman

CASE STUDY 20: "The Credit Carder"
The doctor noticed that some common credit card charges seemed to have doubled. This was especially true for payments to local merchants such as the pharmacy and grocery store, where a team member was often sent to buy office supplies.

The doctor examined the monthly credit card charge more carefully and asked the credit card company to see itemized statements of some of the purchases. Many pharmaceuticals were discovered. The doctor called the local pharmacy to inquire for whom the prescriptions were written. He quickly discovered the name of Julie who worked in his office. She had been using his office credit card to pay for her personal prescriptions at the local pharmacy.

ACTION:
Have the office credit card statement sent directly to the doctor's home. Do not have the credit card left in the office for indiscriminate use. Have the doctor check every itemized charge on the credit card statement each month. Change your office credit card number once per year.

The doctor needs to personally check the credit card statement, bank statement, and cancelled checks monthly. Having the statements sent to the doctor's home instead of the office will help to prevent concealment of embezzlement. Have the doctor personally check the office credit card statement each month for unrecognizable charges and questionable activity. If any transactions are unknown, investigate the activity further.

I know a baseball star
who wouldn't report the theft of his wife's credit cards
because the thief spends less than she does.
– Joe Garagiola

We've all heard the urban legend of a male dentist whose beautiful trophy wife maxes out his credit cards, and then discovers that she no longer loves him, divorcing him when the credit cards are taken away. Or, the beautiful female dentist who finds true love, gets engaged, and schedules her wedding, only to find that her fiancé refuses to sign a premarital agreement to protect her dental office and other assets, including her retirement plan and home.

Embezzlement for a dentist can hit close to home. Both in the office and outside of the office, at home and in society, the dentist is often a calculated target of embezzlers and money mongers. Money can't buy you love. It is therefore prudent for the dentist as well as the HR manager to be cognizant of the greedy lovers of money found throughout society.

CASE STUDY 21: "The Insider"

Dr. X was junior associate in a well-established dental office. He had just completed one year of employment with the senior owner and he was now working his way into a sweat-equity buy-in partnership.

One morning, Dr. X was scheduled to complete a big restorative case. His patient paid off his account with a large payment. The payment was made to the front-office receptionist as soon as the patient entered the office that morning. Dr. X watched the payment transaction as he waited for his patient to be escorted and seated in his dental chair for the start of his dental procedure.

That evening, after the completion of the day's work, Dr. X checked his end-of-day production and collections. He found that no payment had been recorded for his early morning procedure. Then he checked his patient's account. His balance had been adjusted to zero.

Dr. X had a complex problem on his hands. The embezzler could only have been one person, the receptionist, who was the only person at the front desk that day. The problem was, the embezzler was the senior owner's wife.

ACTION:

Dr. X dissolved the partnership and walked away from this business deal. He knew that there was no point in pursuing this partnership further or even discussing it. For all he knew, the senior doctor might also have been involved in this embezzlement situation.

It doesn't matter how payment is made: cash, check, credit card, insurance, or direct deposit. The fact of embezzlement is that a payment has been made which is not in the deposit, and that a write-off is shown. At other times, there could be no contract or data entry at all. The only means of discovering embezzlement is vigilance of systems.

I've always felt there are unacceptable conflicts of interests and risks associated with having a family member (spouse, sibling, child, or step child) working in your dental office. Beside the difficulty of following instructions from family members, insubordination, favoritism, embez-zlement, and the inability to terminate are all potential land mines. Favoritism of relatives, "sycophants," those who flatter, and tattletales have been reported to be the number-one sign of a bad boss.

Max H. Bazerman, in his book *The Power of Noticing*, describes that unethical behavior often can occur on a "slippery slope."

Gradual changes can occur right in front of our eyes, without notice. Experimenters who have studied these phenomena call this "change blindness." Indeed, David Harris of Prosperident confirms that in most cases of embezzlement and dental office fraud, it is a trusted veteran, with at least five, and sometimes twenty years of seniority who is most likely to embezzle. Sometimes a personal life change is exerting financial pressure, and in other cases the embezzler feels that their true value and talents aren't being properly recognized by the doctor or society. Because embezzlement or fraud is created by people who may have been previously considered honest and their change gradual, it is often hard to see.

These statistics are consistent with the "boiling frog" folk tale, which claims that if you place a frog in hot water, it will jump out. But if you gradually turn up the heat, the frog won't notice the change and will be cooked. None of us wants to be cooked by a dishonest team member or those with whom we do business when it comes to fraud and embezzlement. External vigilance is the only preventative measure.

In our increasingly electronic, busy, and complex world, the ways to commit embezzlement are myriad. Indeed, experts in the field would prefer to not commit their experience to paper for fear that potential embezzlers will use their examples for further profit. Provided here are a few common examples for the dentist and HR manager to know that embezzlement is a real-life, *common* problem in the dental office and should be protected against seriously.

There are ways to safeguard against fraud and embezzlement. These include not being overconfident or overly optimistic in your judgments, and to always remain watchful. Prosperident's Embezzlement Risk Assessment Questionnaire (sold on its electronic store at www. dentalembezzlement.com/store) is an excellent, and fairly quick, self-assessment tool. David Harris recommends that doctors complete this questionnaire every three months as a way of keeping in tune with gradual behavioral changes. If you have embezzlement concerns and want to contact Prosperident, their toll-free number is 888-398-2327, and their email "hotline" for someone with a concern who prefers to reach out by email is emergency@dentalembezzlement.com. Or, take the time to attend a Prosperident webinar online or a live seminar in your dental community. It will be a very worthwhile investment.

Chapter 15

POOR WORK ETHIC

Procrastination is the thief of time.
– Edward Young

A poor work ethic wastes time, money, and resources. This is "soft embezzlement," the taking of salary and resources for work not done. These resource wasters make personal phone calls frequently during working hours. They bring homework for night class to do at the front desk during working hours. They plan personal events and family vacations on company time. They check personal emails, or make deliveries off-site to get out of doing in-office work. They run their own errands, or get a manicure or haircut on company time. They may be cleaning their desk incessantly. They waste time, not focusing on patient care.

CASE STUDY 22: "THE WASTER"

Meghan was planning her wedding. While at the front desk, she had a glazed look on her face. She would sometimes simply stare at her fingernails. Her thoughts appeared to be far, far away. The doctor asked her what she was thinking about. She said, "My boyfriend."

One day Meghan was in charge of answering the phone on a non-doctor day. The doctor called in to inquire what was new for the day, and if any patients or doctors had called to speak with him. Meghan did not answer the phone call. The doctor received the "we are busy" phone message. The doctor called three times. Then, the doctor called the neighboring dental office to have their front desk check on Meghan to see if she was OK by herself in the office, or if something had happened to her. Meghan was nowhere to be seen. The office front door was locked.

The doctor called the office manager at home to ask her to go to the office at closing to change the phone message for the next day, and to see if there was any sign of Meghan. The office manager thus traveled to the office on her day off to change the phone message. She noted that at exactly 5:00 p.m. Meghan returned. She had a beautiful new hairstyle and fresh manicure. Surprised not to be alone, Meghan looked at the office manager as she re-entered the office. She then proceeded to clock out.

The next day the doctor gave Meghan her notice with the documentation of failure of attendance as grounds for immediate termination as described in the Team Handbook. A few weeks later Meghan had a new job in a new dental office. The doctor had not called for a reference prior to his new hire.

At the local dental society meeting, the dentist asked Meghan's new employer what Meghan had given him as the reason for leaving her last job. She told him, "It was a girl thing."

ACTION

Time and pay can be embezzled. When this happens, treat it as any other embezzlement, with appropriate fact finding and documentation, leading to termination.

Another means of time embezzlement is "Buddy Punching." Buddy Punching occurs when a missing or late team member has their buddy clock in for them. An American Payroll Association study revealed that "Buddy Punching" is a common occurrence. The statistics of this study showed that it is estimated that over 75% of companies lose money from buddy punching. Employees reportedly *steal* roughly 4.5 hours/week— the equivalent of 6 weeks' vacation. In total, Buddy Punching accounts for approximately 2.2% of gross payrolls.

There are three tools that help companies prevent Buddy Punching.

1. Swipe cards can be issued. Each employee would have their own swipe card to use for a clock-in system. It is unlikely that the swipe card would be available in the office should the employee be running late.
2. A Biometric Employee Time Clock. *This is by far the best tool on the market.* The employee must be present for facial recognition in order to clock in and therefore must be physically present. There are many options on the market today including the Lathem Biometric Face Recognition Time Clock.
3. A "forgot to clock-in function." An employee can still steal time by claiming that they "forgot to clock in." Many tools today will notify employers and employees that they have forgotten to punch-in. Be sure that any software that you use to prevent Buddy Punching also has a "forgot to clock-in" function.

In the dental office, both time and resources can be needlessly wasted. When you see time being wasted on the job in lack of motivation or daydreaming, ask your team member, "What are you thinking about?" If the response is not reflective of a patient or the office, ask the employee to daydream on her own time and give her a new task to complete. Tell her to either focus on work or go home. Ask her to stop wasting your office time and money. Remind her why she was hired, emphasizing that performance is her goal at work and also the reason for her job.

Supplies can also be wasted. It is possible that a Waster may order additional dental products rather than organizing and restocking those which you have already purchased. To prevent wasting, create a notebook and require a signature before ordering additional items. Be sure that items are regularly restocked and inventory taken. Efficiency of systems and lack of waste comes from coaching and supervision.

> *I always arrive late at the office,*
> *but I make up for it by leaving early.*
> – Charles Lamb

Not showing up, coming late, or frequently calling in "sick" are common HR problems. The workforce in our dental offices is small. Every individual counts. Unlike a national chain like Starbucks with a revolving workforce, dental offices usually do not have in-office backup. We therefore need every team member to be reliable.

Not showing up is an action. It is a serious problem. Absenteeism without prior notice is grounds for immediate termination. Absenteeism by the "fly by night" call-in without preapproval should be written up. Absenteeism is also an act for which unemployment benefits will not and should not be paid.

Monday-morning absenteeism is an especially bad sign. As seen in Case Study 14, "The Frequently Missing," not remembering why you were out, if this is truly the case, may be a sign of deeper troubles. It could mean an abusive lifestyle of partying or drug and alcohol abuse. It could be irresponsibility or poor personal lifestyle time management. Or, this person may be a victim of some serious household or other relational problem.

I hope none of us will ever have to apologize to a dental patient for poor customer service saying, "Sorry we're running late today. One of our co-workers called in 'absent.'" Frequent absenteeism eliminates the trust of the team and doctor and ultimately the dental office. It affects the financial bottom line.

Frequent absenteeism also eliminates trust in the perpetrator. When there is a suspicion of unreliability in attendance, there is no acceptance and no trust. Uncertainty and unreliability diminishes team morale. At some point, those who cover for the Unreliable may decide it would be easier not to have this person as a member of the team. The next time this person is absent, the office starts interviewing for her replacement.

A typical workday in the dental office starts fifteen minutes before the first patient. It's great to start with a happy and enthusiastic "Good Morning" and a brief morning huddle. Hopefully the day doesn't start with "Where's So-and-so?" Coming late is temporary absenteeism. It needs to be addressed.

Leaving early is just as bad as coming late. Leaving early without saying goodbye to the doctor and each co-worker or offering to help finish the workload of the day can be a form of participatory absenteeism. Deserting others in need of help is an uncaring act. In an orthodontic office where after-school hours are the most desired appointment times, leaving early is not an option. Lack of punctuality is poor attendance.

CASE STUDY 23: "The Unreliable"

Kathleen was a summer intern. She was assisting during the busy time of the year by answering the phone, scheduling appointments, and performing front-office maintenance duties. On the very first Friday of her employment, Kathleen called in "sick." The dentist called Kathleen at home, but she was unable to speak to him on the phone.

Monday morning, Kathleen returned to work in perfect health. The practice owner sat down with Kathleen and explained to her that unexcused absenteeism causes problems for the dental office in terms of being short-handed. The doctor reviewed with Kathleen that she was hired to work all the days that the office needed her, not just the days that she felt like showing up.

At week's end, Kathleen once again called in "sick" on Friday. Upon return to work, the dentist and co-workers were unable to see any signs of illness. The dentist provided a written warning documenting the second unexcused absence. The dentist also requested a physician's note for the past two illnesses and any other illness in the future absences as stated in the Team Handbook. Kathleen had now been given a verbal and a written warning that her absenteeism was excessive. To be able to return to work and maintain her job, should she be absent again, she would need a doctor's note.

One week later, Kathleen was "sick" again for the third time. A medical note was not produced. The dentist explained to her that Kathleen had been absent one out of four days or 25% of the scheduled work time during her first month. Kathleen was terminated for excessive absenteeism.

ACTION:

Let your team members know that they are missed when they are absent. Let them know that when out, the dentist or office manager will call them at home to see how they are doing. The Team Handbook states that a medical note may be requested for absenteeism due to illness, either physical or mental. Tell the employee that it would be best to show up for work, see how they feel, and if unable to work, they can then make the decision to go home. If feeling sick in the morning, it is also possible for a team member to come to work just for the afternoon. They may find that they are feeling better after a few hours of rest at home.

Document the reason for absence in the employee's private personnel file. Be as specific as possible. Should the reason be sickness or funeral, record the date of the funeral and the name and relationship to the relative deceased. This may be helpful in allowing you to see absenteeism patterns. In this way, you will have documentation and be legally covered should you need to terminate an unreliable employee.

Absenteeism is a major employment problem. Indeed, the Ritz Carlson reports that 20% of their employees are terminated during the first 90 days due to lack of attendance. If a team member is absent during the first 90 days, there is a risk that attendance could diminish even more dramatically after completion of the 90-day introductory period. Be sure to document and evaluate all lack of attendance carefully, especially during this initial period.

> *I can accept failure,*
> *everyone fails at something.*
> *But I can't accept not trying.*
> – Michael Jordan

There is a concept called "social loafing." In the politically incorrect world, some may label it "laziness." However you label it, it's shirking, freeloading, lack of performance, or inability to pull one's weight in the dental office. It is an undesirable work behavior. Particularly in the dental office where teams are quite small, loafing means others need to do more. This activity quickly diminishes team morale, creating office tension and stress.

CASE STUDY 24: "THE MIA"

Where was Meg? Was she in the bathroom, storage room, or her car? Meg could not be found in the dental office. Her break time was over thirty minutes ago. Her patient and doctor were waiting for her and her teammates were looking for her. Meg was once again MIA, Missing In Action.

Later that day, Meg emerged back on to the clinic floor. She stated that she had been visiting the storage unit for the last thirty minutes.

ACTION:

Ask the MIA to be present at work not merely physically, but also mentally, and exhibit enthusiasm for caring for dental patients. Ask the MIA where she goes and what she does when she is away from the office but "on the clock." Tell her that the doctor needs to give permission for her to attend to errands off-site. Include the MIA in all activities. Ask the MIA to work on time management in the completion of tasks. Make her aware of appointments and break period duration. Explain that keeping on schedule and keeping on time is an important task of her job.

Dental offices cannot afford to have an unreliable MIA team member. MIAs need to focus on participation. MIAs need coaching. Help MIAs set goals and priorities. Help them focus on the tasks at hand. Have them keep a log of work they have done for the day. Review their work with them in a one-on-one session. Tracking tasks assigned and completed and instilling accountability will help you eliminate MIA behavior.

Doctors also may have MIA behaviors. They may wander off within their professional building talking to friends or get involved with other projects or work events causing them to lose focus on their patients and the office. When this happens, rein them back in. Focus their attention back to where it should be, in the office, with their patients.

> *I'm not the easiest person to live with.*
> *I'm kind of a slob.*
> – Katie Holmes

We all know them when we see them. They may be perfectly happy, well adjusted, and fun to be around. His disarray may bring him comfort. The Slob is intentional. He displays physical sloppiness such as poor hygiene, bad hair, bad teeth, a wrinkled uniform, shirt not tucked in, pants not hemmed, and maybe even body odor. The Slob can cause problems and stress in the dental office, especially when other team members feel obligated to pick up and straighten up after him.

Signs of the Slob include a messy work area, stacks of disorganized papers, and frequent loss of important items. *Patient records can be misplaced.* The Slob may misfile papers, important books, or office documents. Tasks may not have follow-through, notes may be scribbled, phone messages taken without return numbers. There is little attention to detail with the Slob. Perhaps he is the complete antithesis of the fastidiousness of dentistry. In the dental office, it becomes especially difficult to work with the Slob. Whether the doctor or the assistant, the Slob is a HIPAA violation waiting to happen.

Due to their sloppy habits and work, the entire team will be frustrated with the Slob. The doctor and assistants may become annoyed with the office appearance and effects of disorganization. Because dentistry is a profession of detail, the Slob will need to quickly shape up or ship out.

CASE STUDY 25: "THE SLOB"

Alice forgot to return the office camera after a team outing. Off for the day, the item was needed by the doctor and team and it was in her car. She decided to come from home to the professional dental office building to deliver the missing item during work hours. She strolled into the dental office in her pajamas.

Alice's desk was messy. On another occasion, Alice lost important radiographs in her pile of papers. Then, the doctor's Comprehensive Treatment Planning photographic notebook went missing. The doctor searched everywhere and even called referring dentists and venues asking whether he had left his missing binder. The doctor was perplexed. The binder was later found on Alice's shelf.

After Alice resigned, her work area was cleaned and reorganized. Many missing items were found. Order and peace of mind were restored to the dental office.

ACTION:

Should personal sloppiness exist, set aside time for office cleanup. If sloppiness is in personal appearance and hygiene, send the employee home and tell them to return when their appearance is professional as outlined in the Team Handbook. Give them the assignment of cleaning up their desk within the next 48 hours and instruct them to keep their work area clean and organized. Clearly identify for them a model of desired outcome they need to achieve within a specified period of time. If they can't get themselves together and prove to be a liability to the office, terminate them as quickly as possible.

Some people are at the top of the ladder,
some people are in the middle,
still more are at the bottom,
and a whole lot more don't even know there is a ladder.
– Robert H. Schuller

At the opposite end of the work ethic spectrum is the Career Climber. They're hard working and here for the short-term gain. The upside of the Career Climber is that once hired, she is extremely motivated to learn all that she can very quickly. She will not shy away from any new challenges and projects. The Career Climber is highly intelligent and capable. The downside of the Career Climber is that she generally only looks out for herself and has little regard for her teammates, dentist, patients, or the dental office in which she is currently employed.

The Career Climber will be highly motivated to quickly master every aspect of operations and systems within your dental office. She is highly motivated. She will shine brightly on new projects. All she learns and does will soon lead her to a new and more lucrative career opportunity.

At the interview, The Career Climber will tell you that all she ever wanted in her life was to work in your dental office. Once hired, her story quickly changes. *"I'm not going to be stuck in this job for long"* is the mantra of the Career Climber. The resume of the Career Climber reflects numerous job changes. She will quit for any advancement including a one-dollar per hour raise. Recruiters call this the "The Job Hopper." In dentistry, we may refer to the Career Climber as always having "One Foot Out the Door" at all times.

The Career Climber is extremely common, especially in the Internet age with Millennials, where new jobs can be found instantly online every day. The Hay Group revealed that one-third of surveyed employees in the 21st century worldwide plan to resign within three years. For this reason, if a new employee stays in your office beyond three years, consider them a keeper. If they stay beyond five years, give them an award.

The Career Climber often gets her leads for new jobs from outside vendors and referring offices. Be prepared and have cross-training in place so that when the Career Climber leaves, you can handle the change easily and not be left short-handed. To protect yourself, make sure that the Career Climber does not have exclusive knowledge about any key business operations, computer program, or procedures. Once you know that the Career Climber will be moving on, don't waste additional funds on continuing education. Commit to and develop team members loyal to your dental office for the long term. And never rehire the Career Climber if the rung on the ladder to her next job breaks.

CASE STUDY 26: "THE CAREER CLIMBER"

Za was the keynote speaker at her dental-assisting program graduation. As a hard worker, the Valedictorian with perfect attendance and a 4.0 grade point average, she immediately got a job in the dental office where she interned. She quickly worked her way up the ladder and within six months went from part-time back office to full-time front desk.

Talented, eager, and ambitious, the office continued to cross-train Za for all job functions. She was meticulous and focused. Action was her middle name. The doctor gave her full responsibility and empowerment in line with her position. For her new position, the doctor bought her a new suit and designer pumps. Za looked, felt, and acted as professional as possible. Then the doctor asked her to direct an important dental meeting which the doctor was hosting. Za accepted. Her name was now on the program.

Then it happened. Fifteen minutes before the meeting, Za asked to meet with the doctor in private. She told him that she was requesting a $6.00 per hour raise; otherwise, she stated that she would be leaving. The doctor responded that he would miss her and to please put her resignation in writing. If she chose to have her resignation effective immediately that day, she could leave now.

The Career Climber was stunned. The doctor explained that although she had done an excellent job in the past few months, raises were given based on the overall financial performance of the office as a whole. All employees needed to be considered for raises. The work group functioned as a team and everyone needed to be treated with fairness. Everyone was important and contributed to the overall success of the office. The doctor explained that they had a policy: "Don't tell the doctor that you can get more pay somewhere else, and the doctor won't tell you that he can hire someone for less money than what he is paying you." The doctor explained that everyone was replaceable, even the doctor. As Charles de Gaulle pointed out, "The cemeteries are filled with indispensable men." He thanked Za for the job that she had done while she was at the dental office.

The Career Climber moved on to her new higher-paying job. In her new place of employment she was the only employee. Here, she performed all functions herself. That lasted for a few months and then Za moved on again to yet another work opportunity.

ACTION:

With the Career Climber, it would be best to work with her to plan for this inevitable transition. Openness and respectful communication certainly would make it easier to deal with the Career Climber. If you believe this individual is a long-term asset to your dental office, you can try to develop a career path within your employment framework that would suit her. When there isn't a way to keep the Career Climber, you can discuss that candidly. That way, you have a longer window of time to find her replacement than the standard two weeks when she eventually leaves.

Doctors may receive demands or threats for higher pay. Although this type of behavior is not common, it will happen to you sooner or later, and it is important that you know how to handle it, immediately and unemotionally. *Be strong.* Understand that once special exceptions are made for one person, the news will spread throughout the entire office and the floodgates will open for higher pay demands from the entire workforce. Once pay increase on command precedent is established, and additional demands are unmet, a total team walkout could occur! Be prepared to deal with this type of behavior and have your policy and your mental aptitude in place on how you will handle it with fortitude and professionalism, in a timely manner.

CONFIDENTIALITY –

You may be tempted to have a non-compete agreement to protect confidential information such as patient lists or information when dealing with the Career Climber moving on. Such an agreement is prohibited in California.

Once resignation is received, you have 72 hours to prepare the final paycheck *and a separate vacation paycheck.* Once submitted, you have a choice whether to extend the work time with agreement or make the resignation effective immediately.

Chapter 16

SABOTAGE

The word "sabotage"
derives from ... when workers threw their sabots (wooden shoes)
into the ... gears of the textile looms to break the cogs,
feeling that the automated machines would replace them.
– Adrian Furnham & John Taylor

D ental office sabotage, the intentional damage of property or the subversion of operations, is real. It could take place for the team member to gain a thrill against authority. Or, it could be the cold calculation of a person intent on revenge.

There are many manifestations of sabotage and the underlying causes are multidimensional. Motives can include making a statement, encouraging change, establishing personal worth, or gaining a competitive edge over co-workers. It could be to vent anger created by one's personal life or for some other personal gain. It could also be a cover-up to avoid responsibility for failure.

Saboteurs are often vengeful individuals with a history of complaining and a need to punish those who they see as responsible for their unhappy lot. It is quite impossible to get valid sabotage statistics. First, you're never really sure sabotage has occurred. Second, if it has occurred, do you really want to publicize it? Third, everyone is innocent until proven guilty.

Computer systems present a whole new side of insider threats and sabotage. How many dentists have kept an undesirable individual employed because he or she was the only person who knew the office software? To prevent this, be sure to cross-train everyone in the office on all computer system functions and make sure all entry passwords are recorded. This will help protect you against being held a computer hostage.

CASE STUDY 27: "THE SABOTEUR"

Catherine had a long career working in dental offices. Curiously, her CV did not include an office stay anywhere of longer than five years. Nonetheless, when asked about her past performance, the previous employer stated, "She was very productive. When she left, we needed three people to replace her."

After Catherine's early morning check-in, the computer system often malfunctioned. Brought to her attention usually after subsequent check-ins, Catherine could immediately fix the problem. "Just a loose cord" was often heard. Catherine could immediately fix the problem. She would come in and save the day.

Catherine was not a team player. When involved in cross-training, she would get very angry and state that her teammates were interfering with her job. Catherine also tended to hoard office functions. After four years, all her teammates had to say about Catherine in 360-degree feedback reviews was "She's good with computers."

Catherine's personal life also seemed strained. She lacked family ties and kept to herself. After four years in the office, her personal life was still somewhat of a mystery.

As predicted by her history of short-term stays, after four years, Catherine moved on. Curious thing, once she left, the computer system was never down again.

Catherine moved to a nearby dental practice. Year one passed. Year two brought some added stress and Catherine was reassigned to insurance billing. Year three, the doctor actually paid Catherine to work from home; otherwise his entire team threatened to quit. Then once again, Catherine moved on.

ACTION:

Continuous equipment malfunction could be the work of a Saboteur. Whether intentional or unintentional, keep an eye on computer problems and document incidents and resolutions. What you find may surprise you. Once identified, eliminate the Saboteur from the office as quickly as possible.

Motives

The motives of undesirable workplace behaviors originate for a variety of reasons. In general, causes fall into one of three general categories:

1. Personal: Ranging from beliefs and values to personality disorders
2. External: Family, friends, or criminal influence
3. Revenge: Dull work, lack of recognition, poor management

Perhaps the third cause, revenge, created by a poor dental office work environment can be eliminated through the creation of engaging work, ample team member recognition, and excellent HR management. There is one common threat fostering revenge: eminent termination. Once the decision has been made to eliminate a destructive employee, HR management must be very careful, delicate, private, thoughtful, and humanitarian in manner to orchestrate a safe, timely, and non-dramatic employee exit.

Chapter 17

DYSFUNCTIONAL BEHAVIORS

The stellar universe is not so difficult of comprehension
as the real actions of other people.
– Marcel Proust

I n his book *The One Minute Manager,* Ken Blanchard states that *"We are not just our behavior, we are the person managing our behavior."* When undesirable employee events surface in the dental office, it is imperative for HR leadership to address how this undesirable behavior affects the office, the team, the patients, and the doctor in order to prevent it from happening again in the future. Have a constructive opportunity to talk about what actually happened and how to prevent it from ever happening again. Remind the person involved that they are of value to the team and that you would like improvement leading to elimination of this undesirable behavior. *Actions can be improved.* Addressing the incident will give it the chance of being "nipped in the bud." Not addressing the incident makes HR management part of the problem.

Undesirable actions affect the dental office bottom line. Non-ideal actions or omissions can destroy team effort or break the dental office apart, forcing individuals and doctor to cope on their own. *Some of these poor behaviors can be changed. Others cannot.* Dealing with them wastes valuable time and money on HR management employee rehabilitation.

Behaviors for workplace elimination are negative and express pessimism, anxiety, insecurity, or anger. These may be deliberate acts. They may be hard to describe but we know them when we feel them. When they surface, these actions create a feeling of tension, a feeling of "walking on eggshells" or worry that something in the office is wrong. If this feeling exists, you will need to probe deeper to find the exact root of the problem, and the person responsible for these causative actions. Once discovered, then a solution to the elimination of an undesirable workplace behavior can be accomplished.

> *I don't call it gossiping,*
> *I call it "networking."*
> – Anonymous

"Psst ... did you hear about her?" So speaks The Gossip. Some people don't think gossiping is destructive. They don't realize the damage it does to their own line of work and to their personal reputation. Gossiping is one of the worst of all dental office and life behaviors.

The Gossip talks about people, spreads rumors, and picks apart personal lives. They spread negative tall tales about the doctor, the patients, and co-workers. This behavior is not only a waste of time and money for the dental office, but it can make the entire team including the doctor very uncomfortable.

Gossip can hurt good reputations. The presence of gossiping eliminates teamwork and destroys trust. It can destroy business relationships and friendships. The doctor also must be extremely careful not to talk about employees with other employees. No matter the type of gossip, someone will be disenfranchised. Should this occur in the dental office, ultimately the practice performance and bottom line will be negatively affected.

The Gossip is a liability to any organization. Not only does The Gossip often spread news which is not true, they can cause serious damage to the doctor, co-workers, and the dental office. Negative gossip in itself is a form of organizational betrayal.

Unfortunately, people who take part in the undesirable behavior of gossiping are often socially skilled. They can be charismatic, charming, intelligent, socially poised and self-confident. They can be attractive, popular, and masters of flattery and ingratiation. This personality type comes with a high degree of egocentrism, self-absorption and selfishness. They may also be antisocial narcissists.

In private, the Gossip experiences self-doubt, unhappiness, and low self-worth. Gossip is the means by which they elevate their own self-esteem. They are prone to self-deception and may even believe their own lies. The Gossip lacks integrity.

CASE STUDY 28: "THE GOSSIP"

Dental assistant Joannie loved to gossip. One day she overheard the dentist talking with another assistant about something personal. Although this doctor was a happily married man with children, she imagined that these two were having an extramarital affair. Joannie couldn't wait to share this information with the other team members. Then she decided, why stop there? Why not spread the rumor throughout the entire professional building?

The rumor, of course, was not true. The dentist's wife, who was also the office manager, found out. She was not pleased with this rumor and its instigator: Joannie, the Gossip.

The doctor's wife/office manager and Joannie had a *crucial conversation* about her *action* of gossiping and spreading false rumors. Joannie was demoted from her position of senior dental assistant. This demotion did not please her. At her next annual review, she spoke up about her dissatisfaction with her present work arrangement. The doctor's wife/office manager told Joannie that if she did not like the new situation which she created for herself in the office, she could choose to quit. Joannie replied, "Why don't you just fire me?" The office manager wife replied, "OK then, you're fired." Joannie was dismissed from this dental office where she had worked for nearly twenty years.

ACTION:

Gossiping upsets workflow and damages reputations. This in turn leads to lower productivity. It diminishes the practice's bottom line. Gossiping is a terminable offense.

Tell the Gossiper that it is inappropriate to discuss other people's personal lives or make up false rumors. It is hurtful and makes the Gossip personally untrustworthy. If someone has something of value to say, they should be able to say it aloud so that all can hear. Keep inappropriate thoughts to yourself and keep your nose out of other people's business. Tell the Gossiper to focus on the task at hand.

Should you have an immediate termination due to gossip, have the final paycheck and separate vacation paycheck ready at the time of termination or within 24 hours of termination announcement.

Although we would love to have a "No Gossip Policy" written in our Team Handbook, this is looked at unfavorably and may be considered **illegal** by the National Labor Relations Board (NLRB) under The National Labor Relations Act. *A 'No Gossip Policy" has been found **illegal** in cases in the past.* Such a policy could also be used against a dentist should a legal dispute arise. The National Labor Relations Act states that, "employers cannot create a policy or enforce rules, written or not, which would imply that employees may not gather or discuss their wages, benefits, and working conditions." This statute applies whether the employee is on or off the clock. *This is freedom of speech.*

Employees in a professional small business such as a dental office do not have outright freedom-of-speech rights. The NLRB, through its activist interpretation of the NLRA, is trying to change that. The NLRB enforces the NLRA, which protects workers' rights in terms of freedom of speech. Although you may wish to have an office culture which does not include gossip, this must come from the doctor's example and leadership, and not from written or even verbal admonition against gossiping.

Team training to eliminate gossip is time well spent. Exposure of the evils of gossip will help you to eliminate it; this will yield high performance dividends while building a happy and respectful workplace of trust.

> *Self-love for ever creeps out,*
> *like a snake,*
> *to sting anything which happens ...*
> *to stumble upon it.*
> – Lord Byron

The Narcissist thinks about himself or herself constantly. If you happen to say or do something that the Narcissist finds offensive or experiences as a threat, he or she may attack you venomously. When such an overreaction happens, only an experienced therapist is likely to grasp what that heated response represents.

The Narcissist feels that "if you are not with me, you are against me." He may think that he cannot do any wrong. Narcissistic behavior has been classified as a psychological syndrome. It is serious and one of the few behaviors that CANNOT be modified. It is extremely problematic.

142

The Narcissist is constantly looking in the mirror, straightening her clothes, combing her hair, checking her weight, and questioning what other people think about her. Her conversations revolve solely around herself. Their every action reflects their self-centeredness.

It is difficult for the Narcissist to have close relationships and to connect with people in the dental office. They have a hard time interpreting social cues. The Narcissist will not care about the office, the patients, their teammates, or the doctor. All she will care about is herself.

CASE STUDY 29: "THE NARCISSIST"

Rose thinks that she is the most important and beautiful person in her dental office. She does not think anyone else makes a contribution or does any important work whatsoever. She is very critical of everyone she works with, including the doctor. She points out others' shortcomings in order to make herself look good and to build her own self-esteem.

Rose expresses that she cannot wear the same office uniform that other team members wear because she thinks that it is not stylish or attractive. She asks the doctor to instead order her a designer shirt from Nordstrom's.

Rose is constantly checking her weight through the day. In fact, she carries a little body-fat gauge on her wrist at all times. She checks her body weight between patients. She also checks how far she has walked each day at work in an effort to burn calories on the job. She does not sit at her desk focused on her work performance and patient care, but rather walks through the office in order to record as much weight-loss distance as possible.

The Narcissist's hair is of constant concern. She combs it several times per day. She is often found primping her hair in her office. Occasionally a new patient will compliment Rose on her hair. She will then flirt with the patient to get positive reinforcement on her beautiful appearance.

Rose thinks that some of her long-term teammates should be fired. She does not hesitate to tell the doctor who she thinks should be terminated and why. She puts down other people to build up her own self-esteem.

Eventually, Rose moved on. The entire office team and the doctor breathed a sigh of relief.

ACTION:

Narcissism is an ingrained personality type. It exists along a continuum at which in an extreme state it becomes a Narcissistic Personality Disorder (NPD). In the extreme state, this style CANNOT be modified.

In a mild state, you can try to influence a Narcissist's behavior by being specific about expectations. Tell them to focus on their work and specific tasks and not so much on themselves and their looks. Re-evaluate the response and performance actions to your requests.

You may try adapting to the Narcissist's style. Tell them that it would be *AMAZING* if they would give a Warm Welcome and Fond Farewell to each patient and attend to their individual needs in between. For the Narcissist, patient communication may be difficult.

To keep the Narcissist employed, you may have to ignore some actions and comments made by them. If words and actions are disheartening to the point where team morale is being reduced, you may need to eliminate this person from your dental team.

AGGRESSION

Kids don't want to tattle on bullies.
Neither do the adults.
– Jack Welch

I recently saw the movie, "A Christmas Story." In it, Ralphie and some other small boys are continuously confronted by an older, bigger boy who hides behind a fence and waits to scare and antagonize them. Oddly, this older boy gains pleasure by scaring the younger children.

One day, having decided that he wasn't going to take it anymore, Ralphie confronts the big boy scaring him. There is a confrontation. When the scuffle is over, small Ralphie emerges victorious. Everyone realizes that "The Bully" is actually a coward. The big boy, knowing that his stunt is over, has no reason left for his intimidating actions. Ralphie earns the attention and respect of his peers and his parents. Ralphie's torment stops forever.

The Bully's modus operandi is to hurt the other person's feelings or to discredit them to get their own way or boost their own ego. The easiest, most passive form of this undesirable action in the dental office is "The Silent Treatment." Here, the instigator aims to isolate a co-worker. They imply "Do what I want, or I won't talk to you." A Bully in the workplace pushes at other people in an effort to make them cave in to what he or she wants in order to create conformity and control. A team member uses this form of childish behavior to reject, belittle, and humiliate their teammate. This is psychological warfare.

The most active form of intimidation is sarcasm or humiliation in an effort to isolate an individual. The Bully sets the scene for ostracism. These actions cannot be allowed in the dental office or in life.

Aggression on a behavioral scale can include everything from a single rude comment to chronic workplace harassment, to burning down a dental office to homicide! Aggression can be verbal or physical, passive or active, indirect or direct. Aggression is not part of a healthy environment. It cannot be tolerated in any form. This applies to everyone in the dental office, including the doctor.

> *A study at Arizona State University*
> *revealed that between 25 to 30 percent of all employees*
> *have been bothered by a bully at work*
> *at some point in their working career.*
> – Brette McWhorter Sember
> and Terrence J. Sember

Aggressive behavior may be intentional or unintentional. It is hurtful. Bullying does have two recognizable characteristics: it is unreasonable and is repeated over time. It diminishes productivity in the dental office. If not immediately curtailed, these negative behaviors could grow to even worse actions, which could include cursing, shouting, or even physically striking someone. There needs to be zero-tolerance for bullying in life.

CASE STUDY 30: "THE BULLY"

Michelle picked on Niki in the dental office. She was always quick to point out Niki's "flaws" and undesirable personality traits. Since the doctor and the HR director and office manager *did nothing* to stop this behavior, Niki's choices were to confront Michelle or to quit.

Niki finally asked Michelle that she change her abusive behavior towards her. A heated conversation transpired. Then Michelle physically struck Niki. The doctor arrived on the scene. In an instant, the doctor terminated both Michelle and Niki.

ACTION:

Bullying cannot be tolerated in the workplace. By doing nothing, the doctor and management team have allowed a *hostile work environment* to develop. This is a legal term that opens the doctor to a lawsuit. It's up to everyone in the dental office to make sure there is no hostility in the work environment. Honest and open communication should be able to prevent bad behavior and resolve office disagreements. It is ill-advised to ignore aggressive behavior. When in doubt regarding verbal altercations, immediately call both parties together, facilitate a conversation, and ask questions. Encourage "I" statements, not "She" statements.

Point out that aggressive behavior is unacceptable and has no place in the dental office. Be very clear about what the behavior is. Write up the incident. If not corrected immediately, send the instigator home.

All such incidents need to be reported and documented. This can be difficult, because victims rarely come forward. The innocent party may ask you not to mention it or report it. A Bully may become a person that no one wants to get in the way of. It may be necessary to document events in the personnel file of this aggressor and collect incidents until you have enough evidence for termination.

Watch for the effects of office aggression. If at a monthly team meeting you find that all eyes look to a specific person before anyone speaks, it could mean that everyone is afraid due to one person. If you notice that no one is willing to offer any differing views from a specific team member, this can also be a sign of a Bully.

If you suspect bullying, you need to closely monitor team actions and communication. Listen to and observe what is happening. Once the aggressor is identified, separate her from the team so that her influence cannot take hold. Once confronted face-to-face, eye-to-eye, the Bully may understand that such tactics are no longer successful. It is possible to get this behavior to stop.

> *The two basic power strategies*
> *to try to manipulate and gain control over another person are*
> *silencing and attacking.*
> – Swami Dhyan Giten

Passive-aggression in the dental office can occur through covert sins of omission, such as not delivering messages, not getting part of a job done to help a team member, or doing things to make another look bad. Passive-aggressive people silently compete with and exclude co-workers.

SShhh! Silencing is active-aggressive. Silencing could be not listening, exclusion, ignoring, or not showing respect for another person. It is the silent form of bullying.

CASE STUDY 31: "The Silent Treatment"

Lulu was crying. She had a tiff with her co-worker Winnie over the division of hours on the following week's schedule. When the doctor asked Lulu what was wrong she said with crossed arms, "Nothing." When the doctor asked Winnie what had transpired she said looking the other way, "Nothing." Then the two just stopped talking to each other. They were giving each other "The Silent Treatment."

The doctor told both Lulu and Winnie to go home and get a good night's sleep. She expected both of them to be talking to each other again when they returned to work in the morning.

ACTION:

It you have witnessed this scenario more than once, make the instigator of the Silent Treatment aware that you have seen a pattern in their behavior and actions. Find out who is instigator and who is victim of the Silent Treatment, or whether both parties are at fault. You cannot accept this behavior in your dental office. Don't accept excuses. Tell them that their *actions speak louder than words* and in this case "silence speaks louder than words." Point out the destructive effects of their behavior, its negativity. Let them know that this behavior will not be tolerated.

> *Between stimulus and response there is a space.*
> *In that space is our power to choose our response.*
> *In our response lies our growth and our freedom.*
> – Viktor Frankl

Some people are actively aggressive. They like to argue and start verbal confrontations. They are this way with their families and in their own homes. It is a way of life.

Aggressive employees start altercations with the doctor and other team members; if uncontrolled, they may even argue with a patient. They may verbally harass and damage the team morale, and affect the good reputation of the dental office.

Aggressive behavior may include sarcasm, cursing, or slamming of items or doors. Included in their array of tantrums may be the use of unprofessional language. This cannot be tolerated in any professional setting.

CASE STUDY 32: "THE RED HOT TEMPER"

Iris was a dental-assisting career veteran. Unfortunately, she had a red-hot temper that would surface when she would be in disagreement with a co-worker.

One day, Iris got into a heated discussion with another assistant. It quickly escalated into an argument. The volume rose to a high level and could be heard by all, including the patients, team members, and the doctor. At the climax, Iris actually slapped her co-worker in the face. The dentist arrived on the scene and immediately fired both Iris and her co-worker for unacceptable professional behavior.

Iris got another job quickly because she was very well known in the dental community as a good assistant. Within a few weeks, she got into another heated argument at her new place of employment. This time, the doctor got involved. Feeling uncomfortable with the shouting and violent actions of Iris, the doctor called the police.

The police arrived and escorted Iris out of the dental office. She was, of course, terminated by this office as well. She soon found employment once again in another dental office, which did not call to ask for a reference.

ACTION:

When it comes to HRM, timing is essential. Address and stop problems quickly to restore on-the-spot efficiency, collaboration, peace and harmony. Put out the smoldering fires to keep them from developing into raging conflagrations!

Prevent the Red Hot Temper from escalating into a fire by pointing out that there is no reason to get this upset about anything in the dental office. Pay attention to this behavior and record the history of early signs in your HR personnel records. Tell the Active-Aggressor that becoming angry or raising her voice is unacceptable behavior in the dental office and could lead to termination.

Ask the Active-Aggressive "What is the problem?" They may say, "Nothing; everything is fine." Reply, "No, everything is not fine, because your behavior of anger and shouting in the dental office is unacceptable." Should physical aggression ever be exhibited in the office, make that ground for immediate termination as stated in the Team Handbook.

Talk to the Active-Aggressive about controlling her temper. The HR manager is not responsible for the remedy of the Red Hot Temper. While you may be tempted to send them to counseling, you cannot tolerate aggressive behavior in your dental office or life. They are an active liability, like a volcano, ready to erupt!

> *Good leaders need a positive agenda,*
> *Not just an agenda of dealing with crisis.*
> – Michael Porter

With some, the melodrama never ends. Constantly "sick," boyfriend problems, broken car, out of gas, injured, house on fire, these are the daily events of A Lady of Perpetual Crisis. Being around A Lady of Perpetual Crisis is nerve-racking and anxiety-provoking. The extended friends and family of A Lady of Perpetual Crisis are also in on the act. Parents, husbands, friends, and children have crises of their own as well in which A Lady of Perpetual Crisis is more than happy to participate. Her family and friends enable her and one another.

CASE STUDY 33: "Our Lady of Perpetual Crisis"

Mary was beginning her dental assisting internship. She was absent one day the first week, then another day the second week. Then the third week she called during her lunch break to say that she was unable to come back to work that afternoon after going home for lunch.

The dentist called Mary's home to ask what was going on and determine her fitness for duty. Mary stated, "My parents are having a fight."

The doctor told Mary to come back to her internship that afternoon or don't come back at all. Mary then came back to the dental office with her mother. Mary's mother verbally accosted the doctor, giving tales of Mary's rough childhood. The doctor explained that this was a professional dental office and no place for personal problems and crises. Mary was notified that additional absences would be cause for termination. All incidents were documented and placed in the intern's personnel file.

Mary was dismissed her next missed day of internship. She never completed her internship. She never completed her dental assisting program. She dropped out of school when she unexpectedly became pregnant.

ACTION:
Recognize that A Lady of Perpetual Crisis is a pattern of dysfunction. Review the company policy regarding time off. Tell this personality type that you are looking to hire and retain responsible people. Explain that due to the consequences of their actions in their personal life, they are not able to perform their job duties. With all of their drama, they are unreliable.

Destructive issues cannot be brought to work. Certainly there are changes in individuals' lives, including deaths, relationships, childbirth, illness, or even accidents or fires. But should the team member constantly disrupt the team or be in disarray, it warrants a time-out or dismissal. The decision to end this relationship needs to be made quickly. It may take courage. Shut the door quickly on melodrama. Otherwise, you will become part of it.

Life isn't fair.
It's true, and you still have to deal with it.
Whining about it rarely levels the playing field,
but learning to rise above it
is the ultimate reward.
– Harvey Mackay

The Whiner will take every opportunity to complain and she will question every action in the office. *"Whyyy do we hhhavvve to do it this waaaayyy??"* is the mantra of the Whiner. They block change at every opportunity. Similar to the ever-popular "Grumpy Cat" character, the Whiner never has a smile on her face. She is constantly unhappy and loves expressing exactly how miserable and pessimistic she really feels.

CASE STUDY 34: "THE WHINER"

It was early September and the start of a new school year. The dental office had a big surprise for the boys and girls. It was "Smile Month." The office was decorated with yellow smiley-face decorations. There were yellow bouquets of flowers, yellow pencils and yellow balloons. Every team member was asked to put a smiley-face sticker on her lab jacket and to give a smiley-face sticker and a copy of the poem "Take Home a Smile" to every patient that day. Things just could not have been any more fun! The team gathered at the Morning Huddle in anticipation of this exciting and happy day.

Then it happened. *"Nooooo, I woon't doooo it,"* said the Whiner. What? When asked by your boss to participate, you are unwilling to put a smiley-face sticker on your clinic jacket? You won't join the happiness of the group or share the enthusiasm of the team at the request of your boss, the doctor? *"Nooooo, I don't waaant to!"* said the Whiner.

"Then you're fired," came the doctor's reply. With an expression of shock on her face, the smiley-face sticker quickly went on the lab jacket. A bit overwhelmed or turned off by the office requirement of cheerfulness and active participation in office culture, the Whiner lasted another two weeks before submitting her resignation.

ACTION:

Employment-At-Will can be a wonderful thing. So can "Smile Month." But, whining will never be a welcomed activity in the dental office. This unwanted behavior is common. There are immediate solutions for its elimination.

Some people, no matter how wonderful the dental office, doctor, team, or situation, will find something to whine about. Some people enjoy complaining! This could be the doctor or any member of the team. To help eliminate this unwanted behavior, try replacing it with optimism and joy. Make your office a "No Whining Zone." Peer-to-peer feedback is your most effective anti-whine motivator. If you or someone on your team needs help in this area, please read the book *Learned Optimism* by Martin E. P. Seligman. And ask the Whiner to please bring her enthusiasm to work!

Whining cannot be tolerated. Negativity is miserable to work with and be around. It diminishes team morale and enthusiasm. No one wants to hear it. Tell this person to participate in office activities or choose not to be a member of the team. Participation in patient service (and office culture) is not optional.

Dysfunctional behaviors are difficult to read about. They are difficult to discuss. They are even more difficult to experience. But fear not, you are halfway through. Let's be brutally realistic. You are going to occasionally lose a few people in your quest to make your dental office the best it can be. Sooner or later you are going to hire a dolt or someone who turns your team karma into a raging storm. As soon as you, the leader, realize who is responsible and that an undesirable behavior is being exhibited and ever present, the behavior is either going to change immediately or this behavior will probably need to leave the office. Carry on with courage, communication, and candor.

Too many well-intentioned dentists try to keep disruptive employees from leaving. By doing so, they may be preventing a needed organizational change. This often prolongs the process, or in the worst-case scenario, is the cause of excellent wanted employees leaving. Having the courage to address undesirable work behavior will empower you to transform your dental office into what it could be while restoring organizational health and growth.

Take some time to consider the behaviors mentioned here and to have tough conversations about these behaviors when needed. In the end, these will help you fulfill your office mission and achieve your personal professional core values and goals.

> *Hollow compliments are a sign of immaturity*
> *and justification for why (this) employee*
> *should not be promoted.*
> – John Spector, CEO

A recent website poll by Susan M. Heathfield, HR expert for *About Money* cited that the love of "Apple Polishers" in the workplace is the number-one characteristic of a bad boss. The problem with the Apple Polisher is that they are constantly giving their employer their undivided self-seeking attention while treating their co-workers poorly or in a disrespectful way. Their self-promotion is for their own personal gain and everyone knows it. They are not focused on "We" organizational behavior and are therefore openly rejected by the team.

The Apple Polisher tends to enthusiastically do everything the doctor asks. She volunteers to doctor requests excessively and gives the dentist a continual stream of positive compliments. She may even bring the dentist coffee each morning. However, this employee acts one way to the dentist and a different way to her teammates. The Apple Polisher may make the work environment for their coworkers miserable when the dentist is not present. The Apple Polisher is not authentic.

There will be nonverbal clues when an Apple Polisher is present. At team meetings, eyes roll when the Apple Polisher makes a comment. The Apple Polisher may volunteer when the doctor asks her to do something but never assist when others ask for help. She may openly compliment the doctor but never her teammates. The Apple Polisher goes overboard in giving the boss positive feedback in an effort to "manage-up."

There may be complaints regarding the Apple Polisher's work quality, honesty, or personality. The doctor may be so appreciative of her compliments that he is unaware of what is really going on. Here lies a hidden destroyer of teamwork. This dishonesty is dangerous to teamwork and office morale.

CASE STUDY 35: "The Apple Polisher"

Trudie enthusiastically did everything the doctor asked of her. When asked for help by a teammate, however, she would fail to respond, ignore them, or just walk away. Performing well at her skills-assessment interview, everyone expected an agreeable teammate. What they got was not what they expected. This new hire often flattered the boss, but she rarely gave attention or assistance to her co-workers. The word "We" was not in her vocabulary.

Trudie had integration problems at her last dental office as well. When her lack of teamwork was questioned in private by the doctor, she confided that at her last job she often ate alone and had not been invited to lunch by either her present colleagues nor her past office mates.

As a solution, the doctor suggested that Trudie work to help her teammates. To start, he suggested that Trudie ask everyone in the dental office if they needed help each evening before she left work. It was explained that right now she was the "neophyte," the "new woman in," and it was her job to fit in and be an active member of the team.

Despite efforts to improve, group dynamics with Trudie changed for the worse. There was a chronic tension in the office. Assistants were quiet and unsupportive of the new hire. The dentist really couldn't figure out why because in his arena, Trudie was 100% devoted to everything he ever asked her to do. But out of her boss's sight, teamwork and collaboration were not possible for Trudie. The team was fragmented and office morale suffered.

Trudie finally quit her new office for a higher-paying job in a nearby community. Group dynamics were once again restored after she left and the work environment was once again a happy place. Co-workers now openly communicated and "spilled the beans" about their true feelings and experiences with the Apple Polisher. This was news to the doctor, who thought Trudie had always been authentic in her behavior. He realized now that he had hired a "sycophant," someone who went overboard with compliments for the boss, trying to self-manage themselves upward to gain favor. He was happy that finally positive group dynamics were once again restored.

ACTION:
There is a common-sense solution to the problem of being an apple polisher. Be authentic.

360-degree reviews, two-way reviews between all team members, are vital for feedback and true feelings about areas for teamwork improvement. This review process will give the dentist valuable information about unseen "apple polishing" and other events which may go on out of sight of the doctor.

Ask "What is one thing that each teammate could improve?" Once you have these answers, action can be taken to improve these weaknesses for the benefit of the team. 360-degree reviews can reveal issues hidden from the doctor and give valuable information for performance improvement to help create the best working environment possible.

As the doctor or HR manager, if you find yourself very appreciative of a particular person, it's time to look into the mirror and ask "Why?" You may be missing an Apple-Polishing behavior due to the influence of the positive compliments, lush words, and scenes of adoration. The Apple Polisher is a charmer. Although their rhetoric is entertaining, don't be deceived by their false praise. Continue to encourage excellent organizational behavior to maintain a high level of office performance and morale.

Try honestly to see things
from the other person's point of view.
– Dale Carnegie, Principle 8
How to Win Friends and Influence People

Dale Carnegie suggested that to interact effectively with other people, you have to know their minds. It's hard to imagine or guess another's psychological point of view regarding every workplace conversation. It is also impossible for you to know how another person will interpret your spoken words. This is why it is so important to *be mindful of your spoken words in the workplace.* Beliefs regarding another's perspective are particularly mistaken and magnified in conflict, where views of opposing sides tend to be especially inaccurate.

Discussions regarding physical attractiveness in the workplace can easily cross the line from boisterous, bantering and flirting, to serious, illegal behaviors. A sexual harasser, whether male or female, travels visually and verbally into areas of activity that border on or enter the zone marked "inappropriate." If caught, their behavior may give them the guilty label of a sexual harasser.

Sexual harassment is almost always associated with males in the workplace. It can also be conducted by females. Sexual harassment is often seen as the misuse and abuse of power to humiliate or intimidate another person in the office or seek sexual favors. It can also be used in the opposite direction, insinuated as a threat.

CASE STUDY 39: "The Sexual Harasser"

Doctor Bond returned to his successful dental practice after a ski vacation to the Swiss Alps with his other single male dentist buddies. Anxiously waiting to see him upon his return was his young single dental assistant Kitty. When seeing him, she ran up to him with excitement and publically asked, "So, how do you like them?"

Dr. Bond replied, "Like what?"

Kitty replied, "My new breast implants."

Dr. Bond replied, "They look very nice."

The office manager was standing nearby and overheard the entire conversation. Yet, she did nothing. Another dental assistant laughed out loud. The lab technician quickly came running over to find out what all the commotion was about and to have a look-see. Nothing was done by anyone to discourage the ongoing inappropriate conversation. No history of these events was documented.

Doctor Bond soon tired of the disappointing quality of Kitty's dental assisting. A few weeks later, Kitty was fired for poor job performance. She immediately filed a hostile work environment claim against both Dr. Bond and the dental office stating that she had been unlawfully dismissed. Kitty stated that she had complaints of a hostile work environment where she had been sexually harassed. She claimed she was unfairly fired in retaliation for speaking out.

Dr. Bond and the dental office were brought to court on grounds of sexual harassment and unlawful termination. This cost the doctor and the office valuable time and money.

Kitty was given a state-appointed attorney for free. She was now unemployed and suffering additional psychological damage from the incident.

The jury listened to both sides of the story. Both sides had witnesses. Both sides had stories. Who is guilty? Who is innocent? What's the verdict?

The subsequent investigation revealed that Kitty had initiated inappropriate office conversation. Witnesses testified this to be true and the doctor had a good attorney. But, this case could have gone another way.

ACTION:
Is harassment training offered to employees in your dental office? Have you handed out any harassment brochures or reviewed any harassment videos? How often? It is best to have a zero-tolerance policy regarding topics considered inappropriate conversation in the dental office.

It is prudent and wise to stay away from topics sexual in nature. Many dirty jokes could get one in trouble. Touching or hugging over and over could also be viewed as "pervasive and persistent" sexual harassment. In general, it's better not to touch your co-workers or employees.

To be safe, stay away from making comments on body form or sexual attractiveness to a co-worker. Sexually abusive language or inappropriate images in the workplace are inappropriate. All questionable comments and behaviors must be addressed immediately and not condoned by management. Outrageous touching of an inappropriate body area can really get you into trouble, even if it is just once.

If a claim is entirely made up, in bad faith, the truth should set you free. Our legal system should ferret out baseless, false and made-up claims of harassment if you follow the rules. Be sure to always document incidences of questionable workplace behavior. Without proper documentation, you could be reduced to a "he said, she said" situation. Have guidelines set in your Team Handbook. Follow employment laws.

Court proceedings entail scrutiny and cross-examination, and test authenticity and accuracy. Follow proper employment procedures and there is a higher probability that you will prevail in a court of law should trouble of this nature arise.

Harassment is defined in the Webster's New World Dictionary as: Har-ass 1 to trouble, worry, or torment, as with cares, debts, repeated questions, etc. 2 to trouble by repeated raids or attacks, etc.; harry. For employment, forget the dictionary definition. Harassment is prohibited conduct related to hiring and firing decisions.

In the workplace, there are two possible forms of harassment. The first is Sexual Harassment with implied *quid quo pro*. This would include unwelcomed sexual advances, requests, or conduct used for an employment decision. The second is a Hostile Work Environment of harassment including intimidating, hostile, or offensive working conditions which interfere with an individual's work or performance. Hostility could be based upon race, age, disability or other factors.

Could one incident suffice as harassment? The EEOC says *YES*. "The Commission will presume that the unwelcome, intentional touching of a charging party's intimate body areas is sufficiently offensive to alter the condition of her working environment and constitute a violation of Title VII."

> *The truth will set you free,*
> *but first it will make you miserable.*
> – James A. Garfield

No one likes to be misled. A liar makes promises they never intend to keep and they cover up their mistakes. They hold up one hand to solemnly swear while holding the other hand behind their back with fingers crossed. In the dental office, they may say work is done when it is not done. They may blame others for their mistakes.

For the HR manager or dentist, one problem in gaining perspective on how to improve the dental office is that others won't tell you what you need to know. You may ask a specific question, such as "Is this or that done?" If the response is a lie, misleading, or misdirected in an effort to avoid, or not divulge the truth, it is impossible to make effective office changes. You can't fix what you don't know is broken. Thus, the team mantra "Only the truth shall be spoken" is paired with the constant need for checks of all systems.

CASE STUDY 37: "The Liar"

Winnie knew she was behind on her work. She had a stack of dental referral letters to be written and mailed out to referring offices. The doctor asked, "Are the referral letters done?" Winnie replied. "Yes. I'll be all caught up on my work by Friday. You have nothing to worry about."

This situation went on for several weeks. It wasn't exactly the truth about the state of dental office affairs. Winnie hid her work from the doctor and the team for as long as possible, telling them that everything was up to date and assuring them that she was doing a great job.

Once Winnie departed for a new job in a distant location, her letters still needing to be written were discovered in a stack in her desk drawer. Now knowing the situation, the dentist immediately hired a transcriptionist. All letters were done within one week.

All Winnie needed to do was *tell the truth and ask for help*. She would have received help and been caught up on her job duties. It took the office only one week to catch up.

ACTION:

Ask team members regularly if they need help with the completion of their weekly tasks. Tell them to be honest about what needs to be done. Tasks may need to be shared, reassigned, or help given, should completion of a task become difficult or impossible.

If a person lies ask them why. Were they fearful of losing their job? Assure them that you want only the truth no matter how severe, and tell them that they are safe and that you are all on the same team.

The good news is cynicism regarding liars can be kept in check. Studies have shown that the vast majority of lies are told by a small number of chronic liars. Most people will tell you the truth if you ask a direct question when you are open to hearing an honest answer. The main reason people lie is to avoid being punished. Relieve the fear of punishment and you are removing the barriers to hearing the truth. Consider an office policy of complete immunity as long as you tell the truth.

Have an office honor code that only the truth shall be spoken. Review this with your team members regularly. Have the doctor tell the team the truth, whether good or bad, and set the standard of candor. It may be miserable at first, but without knowing the truth, situations and problems cannot be corrected and help cannot be given.

If lying is an inbred tendency, then you have a bigger problem on your hands. Bring the lie to the attention of the liar. If lying is the problem, and not the work performance, tell the Liar if their behavior does not change, you will need to change their role, relationship, or perhaps dismiss them from the office.

> *Being in a band you can wear whatever you want –*
> *it's like an excuse for Halloween every day.*
> *– Gwen Stefani*

"Girl with the band," and rock 'n' roll in itself is not the problem. It's the side effects of the bad habits of many of the people in this environment that get this kind of team member into trouble. Beware of "The Monday Morning Flu," trembling hands, and dilated pupils.

CASE STUDY 38: "THE GROUPIE"

Linda was an attractive, divorced mother of two. She had completed her dental assisting internship and was given an excellent work reference by this doctor. She was hired by a local pediatric dental office and worked there for a few years. She was then hired by an orthodontic office. The doctor praised her for excellent work and often cited her as an example of an outstanding and devoted chair-side dental assistant. Linda's work status was very good.

But Linda had a problem: an out-of-control boyfriend with very bad habits. One day the doctor spotted Linda and a police officer in the parking lot. A purse was being emptied onto the hood of the officer's police car. The doctor thought, "Linda must be helping the police officer by turning in a lost purse. She is such a good citizen! Now they are looking for information in the purse to find its rightful owner."

Next the doctor saw that Linda was being handcuffed! He spoke out: "Is everything O.K.?"

The officer shouted, "Get back!"

With her head bowed in shame Linda could only say, "I'm sorry, doctor."

Next, two undercover DEA agents and state dental-assisting board officials were in the doctor's office. They explained that Linda had been under surveillance for suspicion of ordering drugs at the pediatric dental office where she had previously worked. This office was tagged by computer surveillance for having excessive narcotics. Linda had been found with these in her purse, and her apartment had been raided. These orders were found in her apartment. Linda was now going to jail.

The doctor was told that if he had not been an orthodontist, a dental specialist who does not order or prescribe any prescription drugs, that he would have had three years of his own office orders under investigation. Being an orthodontist had prevented that.

In shock, the doctor asked how he could have been able to tell that Linda had this problem. The DEA agent told him, "Look for dilated pupils."

Having been bailed out of jail by her parents, Linda called the dentist stating how much she loved her job on his home-answering machine. The doctor never returned her call.

Years later, Linda visited his office as a happily married mother of three and someone very active in community events. She had gotten her life together.

ACTION:
You may want to include a pre-employment drug test as part of your employment policy. This may not prevent a future problem from ever entering your office but it certainly will discourage users from applying for a job in your office.

Illegal prescription orders are also a form of dental office embezzlement. Be sure to audit these invoices at least quarterly and keep careful records. Take care to lock prescription pads securely away.

It's sad that we live in a society where it may be necessary for an employer to check for dilated pupils. Recognize that shaking hands as well as many other signs can indicate a drug-addiction problem. Have it written in the Team Handbook that failure to return to work without good reason is job abandonment and grounds for termination.

Life is too short to spend in negativity.
– Hugh Dillon

The Poisoner will thwart all change, new ideas and fresh projects. Negativity is their middle name. They predict that the ideas of others won't work. They hold back the organization in which they work with constant pessimism. They are miserable to be around and are to be avoided like the plague.

They can turn a team meeting into a negativity-fest. No solution is ever right or good enough. The glass is always half-empty. It is painful for them to ever say anything nice. Left uncontrolled, they spread gloom and despair to other team members. Their negativity can be highly contagious.

CASE STUDY 39: "THE POISONER"

For many years, Penny had struggled with a poor attitude. One day, the doctor had a new idea for a schedule change. Since many employees in California now had Fridays off due to a statewide furlough, the doctor decided to change the four-day workweek schedule from Monday through Thursday to Tuesday through Friday in order to accommodate more patients being off work on Fridays.

The new Friday schedule would be 8:00 a.m. to 1:00 p.m. The team would still have Friday afternoon free. It was a great schedule for everyone in the office and for the community which they served.

The doctor announced the change at the next monthly team meeting. All were excited about the news. All except one. Then it came, like a dark cloud of rain on a cheerful parade, "I can't do that. It's a bad idea. No one wants to go to the dentist on Fridays. It won't work."

For a moment the air came out of the party balloon. It was once again, the Poisoner.

The doctor called Penny aside "If you can't work Fridays, we'll need to start interviewing for your Friday position. It will probably be hard to find someone for just one day."

Soon Penny was gone. The Friday work schedule was popular and productive.

ACTION:

Tell the Poisoner to contribute to solutions, not problems. Ask them to do this in a positive way. Remind them to be a team player. Reward optimism and discourage pessimism. Otherwise, the choice is given to either come on board with the new change or step down from their position.

> *If you work just for money,*
> *you'll never make it,*
> *but if you love what you're doing*
> *and you always put the customer first,*
> *success will be yours.*
> *– Ray Kroc*

Some people do not want to work; some people love to work. Some may not even need to work; some need to work yet wished they didn't. Whatever your situation, at the dental office, please surround others with your joy for being there. Constant talk of retirement is annoying. Don't just work to get out of your house. Make the world a better place by your presence.

CASE STUDY 38: "The AARP Hopeful"

Peter kept talking about retirement at work. He was financially well off with a successful practice, spouse, no mortgage, and children through college. Everything he owned was paid for and he had a good retirement plan and savings. Sometimes he would discuss other activities he could pursue instead of working as a lab technician at the dental office, like fly-fishing or camper travel. For others, around him, it was annoying. The doctor received several complaints from team members with the suggestion that if Peter really didn't want to work or have to work, maybe he should just retire.

The doctor met with Peter one-on-one and explained that his constant talk of retirement was not an uplifting daily conversation for his teammates. Peter appeared sad. He stated that he loved his job and didn't even realize that he was even having this daily conversation or the negative effect that it was having on his teammates. He said he was sorry and he stated that he would not do it again.

Peter's retirement talk ceased instantly. He was once again a highly valued and popular team member. He continued his career another ten-plus years to what turned out to be a very long and successful career in dentistry.

ACTION:

Retirement can be a very good thing. Many people in dentistry never want to retire. If you suspect that you may have an AARP hopeful in your office, tell them your goal is to have "the happiest office on earth." Ask everyone in your office no matter what their tenure to focus on what they love about their job and to consider the "I love my job" mentality.

To really enable someone in your office to change undesirable work behavior into the desirable work behavior you would like, you not only need to be clear, you need to be painfully clear. You need to verify that your understanding of the situation is correct and express the concerns that are on your mind. Communication leads to collaboration. Understanding other people requires getting their perspective, listening, and expressing that which is to be achieved. Being transparent as the HR manager often eliminates misunderstanding and strengthens the social ties that make office life better.

Warning Signs

Undesirable workplace behaviors must be identified and understood in order to be eliminated. Here we have reviewed some of the warning signs. Your goal as an owner or HR manager is retention of high performers, maintenance of high morale, and inspiration of your team in a positive work environment. It is your duty to turn over low performers, dysfunctional people, and creators of low morale. This will be done by taking charge, managing change, and yet being interpersonally sensitive. It is important to stay calm under pressure, be organized, and take action. This is the mastery of the HR management challenge.

With your help, a mindful well informed employee may even recognize their own need to take a "time out" to reprogram their behavior. You will need to address every issue and document each face-to-face conversation. When there is no chance of improvement or if matters get worse, you will need to give warnings and timelines for change.

The ultimate consequence of repeated undesirable workplace behaviors is termination. Get professional advice for this final event. You may want to have the presence of a third party when it comes time to say good-bye.

As you spend less time putting out HRM fires, you will have moved closer to your ultimate dental office workplace paradise. Once undesirable behaviors are eliminated, you will have quality time with your high-performance team.

Marcus Buckingham and Curt Coffman, in their classic HR book *First, Break All the Rules* outline the experience and knowledge summarized by the Gallup Organization's poll of 80,000 managers of over 400 companies on HRM. The essence of their insight is to focus on talent and eliminate undesirable workplace behaviors. Their wisdom is summarized by the following statement:

> *People don't change that much.*
> *Don't waste time trying to put in what was left out.*
> *Try to draw out what was left in.*
> *That is hard enough.*
> – Buckingham & Coffman

Part Six

HR MANAGEMENT

When you discover your mission,
you will feel its demand.
It will fill you with enthusiasm
and a burning desire to get to work on it.
– W. Clement Stone

E ach team member needs to *be the mission* of their dental office. Jack Welch wrote that the mission is the defining moment for a company's leadership. Peter Drucker wrote that a mission statement should be succinct and fit on the back of a t-shirt. At Gorczyca Orthodontics, our mission is simple "Caring professionals serving valued patients." This statement is short yet robust.

In order to be the mission, each team member needs to first have a mission, to feel it, to embrace it, and then to implement it through their performance actions.

Core values are *the how of the mission.* They are behaviors, the actions you want in your team. At Gorczyca Orthodontics, our core values are clinical excellence, outstanding customer service, and a great patient experience. Reciting these statements of the mission and core values are part of our annual review process. Knowing and maintaining these statements makes you part of our team.

Chapter 18

ACCOUNTABILITY

*It is time to restore the American precept
that each individual is accountable for his actions.*
– Ronald Reagan

When individuals are responsible for a certain job and the results of that job are measurable, there is accountability. It is demonstrated at team meetings and fuels performance. Accountability is follow-up on the implementation and completion of individual tasks which have been carefully created at the previous month's meeting planning session. Individual accountability calls for identifying and addressing all situations. When everyone is accountable, action will be more readily taken for positive change.

TARDINESS
I personally learned about time accountability the hard way. My team decided they would write me up whenever I was late. The results at my annual review were embarrassing. That exercise changed my tardy habit forever.

Are you accountable for being on time in the morning? Are you accountable for returning from lunch on time? If someone is late in the morning, dissect the problem and come up with a solution. Work backwards. Set up a schedule:

8:00 a.m. Out of bed
8:45 a.m. Leave home
9:10 a.m. Walk in front door of dental office
9:30 a.m. See first patient

Another possibility is:

6:00 a.m. Out of bed
6:45 a.m. Leave home
7:00 a.m. Drop off children at school
7:40 a.m. Walk in front door of dental office
8:00 a.m. See first patient

When accountability is broken, do you have the same conversation again and again? How many times? You have to be the judge of when lack of accountability is not in line with the job requirements. Once someone gets written up or fired for lack of accountability, everyone else will quickly get the message.

In most dental offices, schedules are choreographed to ensure that patients are served during agreed-upon times. Late individuals upset the schedules and interfere with the ability of the dental office to get through the day in a smooth manner. If people continue to be late—after being warned that further tardiness will put their jobs in jeopardy—then termination may be the only solution.

I once had a team member whose sister, while working for a large corporation, returned late from lunch. She was immediately sent home for the rest of the day, without pay. This action certainly got across the message that tardiness was not accepted.

In the best dental offices, everyone communicates openly and holds everyone else responsible for their own actions regardless of job or position. This includes the dentist, the manager, and all members of the dental team. This level of high-functioning teamwork is based on conversations. This communication starts with the morning huddle. It then continues throughout the entire day. It ends only after the last patient is out the door and everyone has pitched in together to get the office ready for the next day.

Once understood and agreed upon, it's important that broken rules be openly discussed. When seen, all team members need to have an obligation to speak up. What you don't want is a silent team, one without action, which does not hold all others accountable, where the boss, most often the dentist, is expected to enforce all office rules alone.

People tend to become more
emotionally intelligent
as they age and mature.
– Daniel Goleman

EMOTIONAL INTELLIGENCE

Emotional intelligence (EI) is often considered to be the ability to handle stress effectively and to control emotions adaptable to fit the situation. All dental team members, including the doctor, are responsible not only for measurable performance standards, qualities, and actions but also for their emotional behavior in the office. We must be able to use emotional awareness information to guide our thinking and behavior, so as to create a great working environment. This creates an office culture and best serves the patient. Often, we must put our own feelings aside in order to provide great customer service and an enjoyable, relaxed patient experience in the most caring and professional way possible.

CASE STUDY 41: "THE AWOL"

Margaret, the front desk receptionist, received a personal phone call in the dental office during patient hours. Her medical test results presented some upsetting uncertainty. Emotionally distraught, she stood up from behind the front desk, and without warning or explanation, walked out the front door. She went AWOL, "Absent Without Leave." The front desk was left unattended. Her teammates, in a state of emergency and confusion, covered for her.

The next day, Margaret returned to work. She explained that she had gone AWOL because she had received an upsetting medical test which needed her immediate attention. She was given the directive that, should she receive disturbing news, to please express herself and work with the team to find an immediate solution to her "request" for leave.

169

ACTION:
Emotional Intelligence in the small dental office is a prerequisite for long-term success. When absent, lack of emotional intelligence is the path to failure. If a first-time AWOL offender is not a long-term team member with an excellent prior track record, desertion of their post is grounds for immediate termination, as described in the Team Handbook. Be aware that this behavior could occur again. If this is someone who has a good track record and this is their first issue, you can write up this action, letting them know your future expectations.

The business costs of emotional upset are high. Talk to your team about how such adverse reactions are a danger to the patients and the dental practice by creating a loss of trust. Ask team members to control their emotions, no matter how difficult.

On the opposite end of the spectrum, this case scenario could have been worse. Regarding Margaret's distress, she could have "let it all hang out." The free reign of feelings is also not emotionally intelligent. *What we want is to manage our feelings so that they are expressed appropriately and effectively, enabling people to work together in the best way possible.*

Emotional Intelligence is of utmost importance in leadership. Daniel Goleman, in his book *Emotional Intelligence,* states that for people in business, emotional intelligence does not mean merely "being nice." At strategic moments, it may demand *not* "being nice," but bluntly confronting someone with an uncomfortable truth. He also states that women, in general, show more empathy, and are more adept interpersonally while men, in general, handle stress better.

> *Peace is not the absence of conflict,*
> *it is the ability to handle*
> *conflict by peaceful means.*
> – Ronald Regan

CONFLICT RESOLUTION
Subtle signs of underlying conflict in the dental office include glaring and unfriendly body language, such as the crossing of arms or "the meet-

ing after the meeting." There is a feeling of tension. Sometimes we say we need to speak about "the elephant in the room."

You may experience signs of withdrawal from conflict. These include lack of attention and eye contact, eye rolling, looking elsewhere (such as out the window), crossed arms, or picking of fingernails.

It's important to find out what is going on in a less-than-ideal work episode where disagreement may be present. It is the doctor's or office manager's responsibility to discover the truth and help the innocent party. You may not be able to immediately identify that person, so you need to ask questions to find out who started a conflict situation.

There are two possibilities in a conflict.

1. One person is responsible.
2. Several team members have bad attitudes that day.

Maybe one person is rallying the entire team to make it "Pick on XXX day" or "Complain about XXX day."

Maybe there are non-participating persons trying to survive a bad attitude. It is your job as the HR manager to discover the source and put in place a solution.

When you address disagreement, encourage "I" statements. You will hear "She did this," and "She did that," or "It's her fault." Ask individuals to describe their own behavior with an "I" statement. Tell your employee to discuss and concentrate on her own actions and not others.

An unstable situation that may produce conflict can especially be present when a new hire joins the office. People who have worked together for years may have their own way of doing things. Now enters a new personality. If the new team member is excellent, there may be jealousy. If the new team member is a weak link, there may be disappointment and pressure for the new person to shape up fast.

New actions may surface if individuals need to boost their egos. A "ringleader" may surface. Just being aware that this may happen will help you prevent it.

It is always best to address unwanted behaviors with candor. Dental offices are small and all parties need to work together. Maintain an ongoing dialogue between everyone in the dental office so they can all work well together in a cooperative and professional way.

Disciplining yourself to do what you know is right and important,
although difficult,
is the high road to pride, self-esteem, and personal satisfaction.
– Margaret Thatcher

CORRECTIVE ACTION

Managers and doctors who *don't* bring misconduct or low levels of performance to the attention of their team do this at their own peril. Due to their own lassitude, the incidence of these unfavorable actions will escalate. *They are part of the problem,* not the solution. They are contributing to the creation of a less than ideal workplace.

You may need to take corrective action with someone to get your point across for desirable behavioral or performance change. Don't look the other way and hope that performance will improve. Chances are, it will not. Consider that this individual needs your guidance. Explain the desired behavior, document the discussion, and give the employee the opportunity to improve.

Means of corrective action may include:

1. Verbal Reprimand

Consider this verbal counseling. "XYZ is an unwanted action. Let's put together a plan to improve or eliminate XYZ. Let's see if we can eliminate XYZ and create ABC in the next 30 days. Presently, you are valued in our dental office. Let's work together to achieve the specific office expectation for your desired performance. The next time you do XYZ, which is an undesirable behavior, I will need to write you up."

Document your conversation and place a note in the personnel file. It will be up to the leadership of your dental office how many times the same verbal reprimand will be given. At-will employment does not require any progressive steps prior to termination.

2. Written Reprimand.

Written counseling is more serious in nature. This written document will outline the team member's shortcoming and give suggestions for improvement and a date of the next review. It will be reviewed with the team member in a private one-on-one session in the office. This document should leave not room for misinterpretation. The employee should know that this is their last warning.

"After verbal warning, XYZ was repeated again on such and such a date. This is the last written warning before termination." This document will be signed by the team member and HR manager or doctor and placed in the employee's personnel file. The employee will receive a personal copy.

Voluntary Termination

Unless you're Donald Trump, no one likes to terminate a team member. Voluntary termination in difficult situations following a reprimand is a win-win. The employer kindly eases the employee out of the office while the employee gets to appear that the termination was all their idea.

The action of a reprimand more than anything makes it clear that it is the team member's last chance to correct his or her behavior before termination. Many team members who are unable to improve their behavior or performance will at this time resign voluntarily.

Reprimands may include:

1. Reducing pay
2. Reducing hours
3. Demotion in title
4. Removing responsibilities
5. Removing privileges

After requesting the desired performance change, you may need to place someone on a 90-day probationary period. Have the team member sign the written reprimand as their last warning.

Every person deserves the opportunity to change his or her behavior or performance. Assign a limited period of time for the change to happen. Thirty days is more than adequate time. After the second offense and written reprimand, you may want to dismiss the team member.

DISMISSAL

Have the dismissal documents and the final paychecks ready prior to dismissal. *Write a separate vacation paycheck* and have it ready before the time of dismissal. Have the dismissal documents signed at the time of the final dismissal meeting. Be sure to obtain the office keys before the team member's departure. Otherwise, it will be necessary to change the locks on the office doors. Request the return of all office uniforms.

Escort the team member to the front door and say thank you. Always be professional and polite. Be as nice as possible. Discontinue their alarm code and any office communication including email. Change computer passwords.

There are things that the departing team member may say at their exit interview that you need be aware of. Here are a few examples:

Question 1: "So I get paid for my unused vacation time, right?"
Answer 1: Yes, *here is your separate vacation paycheck.* Please sign this document to verify that you have received it today.

Question 2: "Are you replacing me?"
Answer 2: Do not answer. This is none of the departing team member's business.

Question 3: "Am I being dismissed because I am a woman, pregnant, old, disabled, or a minority?"
Answer 3: Definitely *NO.*

THOSE WHO STAY BEHIND

Dismissing someone will be difficult for those left behind. In some cases, it may take a psychological toll. In other cases, it may be a relief. In either case, it would be a good idea to have an informational get-together with the team to improve the aftermath bonding. Meeting after work at a local café would help to clear the air. This will be psychologically beneficial for all involved.

Team members who may remain friends with the departed employee should be asked to not pass on any further information about the office in form of patient lists, documentation of mailing lists or strategies, or financial information. There is a strict prohibition of company secrets taken by physical or electronic means. Although you may want to tell your team members not to talk about the office with departed team members, this cannot be enforced.

PERSONNEL FILES

For the privacy protection of each team member, personnel files need to be locked at all times. You may even want to keep these records off-site and out of the office. This information could also be kept on the computer. You may want to hire a company to handle HR personnel files for you. One such company is HR for Health. They can be reached at www.hrforhealth.com.

Personnel files hold valuable information about dismissed employees. Should you have dismissed team members, you may want to consider storing these personnel files off-site or scanned in computer format. This file may need to be accessed. It is best to keep these records and payroll information for seven (7) years.

California requires that employers give a copy of the personnel file to any current or former team member within 30 days of request. This also includes required personnel file access by representatives of the present or departed person. Failure to follow through on personnel file duplication within thirty (30) days may lead to employer fines.

Chapter 19

REVIEWS

*There are only three measurements
that tell you everything you need to know
about your organizations' overall performance:
employee engagement, customer satisfaction, and cash flow.*
– Jack Welch

How do you rate each individual in your office? Do you outline personal areas for development and set independent career goals for the coming year? Are individual achievements linked to the success of your dental office? What office activities indicate that this is so?

An epic leader in human resource management, Jack Welch, CEO of General Electric considered 10% of employees the best, 70% critical or being developed, and 20% redundant (the worst). Jack Welch had intolerance for failure and mediocrity. To not discuss deficiency was what he called "superficial congeniality." He emphasized that there were times when people would need to go, for the improvement of the company.

Annual Reviews
Annual performance evaluations are a means of communication, improvement, development, and individual growth. Formal one-on-one meetings can be conducted least one time per year. These need to be summarized on paper and a copy given to each team member. These

177

appraisals will be stored in the personnel file. They may be used as reference at a future time.

There are two good HR management annual review options:

1. Conduct the performance appraisal on the anniversary date of hire.
2. Pick one day per year and review all evaluations on that same day.

For time and efficiency's sake, we have found it easiest fulfill the annual review process on one full day. We choose a date during the second half of the year, usually in November. This is a quiet office season, which includes the grateful time of Thanksgiving. What better time of year to conduct evaluations and initiate ideas for the new year. It's also a great time for one last motivational push focusing on year-end results.

Standard reviews are usually independent of pay raises as described in the Team Handbook. These forms are available from gneil.com, 800-999-9111, as well as other sources mentioned in this book. It is best to have forms that are attorney approved. They may include generic performance factors such as quality, productivity, job knowledge, reliability, attendance, and independence, as well as contributions, initiative, following rules, relationships, and judgment.

Be sure to communicate frequently with individual employees about their performance, not just during the season of formal performance evaluations. What is said at this meeting should not be a surprise to anyone. *The appraisals should be based on an entire year of work and not just occurrences from the last few weeks.*

The gathering of periodic information can be summarized in a Supervisor's Journal. This tracking tool will include a calendar and performance notes for persons in your office. Regular data entry will enable you to quickly see patterns of behavior and give you a permanent account of the history of happenings in your dental office throughout the entire year. Be sure to also include your own performance in the journal if you are the HR manager or doctor. A Supervisor's Journal is available from gneil.com, 800-999-9111, or hrdirect.com.

Carefully review your notes and collected information before filling out your annual performance appraisals. *Use performance information, not feelings or opinions.* Include supporting facts and actions. *The review should be pleasant and not have any surprises for the team member.* Problems are best addressed near the time when they occurred. What can be beneficial to point out are patterns of behavior and areas for improvement, development, and growth.

Have team members complete a self-appraisal. Have them rate their own performance. Have the doctor do a self-appraisal as well. This will illuminate valuable information about performance from the individual's perspective. This can be insightful and eliminate misunderstanding. Ask each person what his or her vision is for the practice. It may surprise you to find that most of your team members will grade themselves a lot harder than you might grade them or vice versa.

If you are the doctor and you do a self-review, give yourself the lowest grade of anyone in each category. You, after all, are responsible for the individual performance of each person you employ. *Their failure is your failure.* Review yourself first and share the results in an open discussion with your team. This will build trust and communication with your own team members and make them more open to accepting their own constructive ideas for development, which you are about to deliver in their individual evaluations.

Clear your desk and clear your mind before the time of the reviews. Set aside a special day for annual reviews. Give the annual review process the attention it deserves. *Give each team member your full attention and respect.* Hold quality two-way discussions.

Do not rush the review. Be sure to ask each team member for his or her opinion on how the office can be improved. During the review, stay clear of feelings and attitudes if possible. These feelings are difficult to substantiate. Ask team members for their creative thoughts and feedback. Reviews will help you set the path for the coming year. This is valuable information you can use for office improvement.

THE S. M. A. R. T. METHOD

Try using the S. M. A. R. T. method to rate job performance. Here is how it works.

S – Specific: "Let's improve your customer service score to 10."

M – Measurable: "Let's collect customer service surveys each week."

A – Achievable: "We may not get a 100% rating of "10" for customer-service scores, but let's try to have the majority be a score of 10."

R – Realistic: "You can certainly hand out one service satisfaction survey each day."

T – Time-based: "Let's improve customer service to a 10 within the next three months.

Let's meet again in three months to review our progress on your improved customer service score."

Be sure to make all of the plans for growth and development stated in the reviews real and tangible. You may want to set up a 30-, 60-, or 90-day individual follow-up. This would be the next date when the team member would be held accountable for the plans and commitments that have been agreed upon.

Once each review is completed, be sure to have each team member sign the appraisal and make a copy for them to keep. Store each original appraisal in each team member's confidential personnel file. Remember that intermittent review sessions need not be lengthy or seen as an onerous chore. Occasional impromptu sessions can be 15 minutes or less. Time limitation enhances focus and promotes efficient productivity.

360-Degree Reviews

The 360-degree system gives the individual and the organization as much information as possible from many sources. A 360-degree review includes feedback to the team member from the doctor, other team members, referring dentists, patients, and sales reps. This meeting takes more time but it will give valuable feedback. It will also evaluate the level of customer service and teamwork delivered by the individual.

Imagine if a sales rep tells you that she thought that the receptionist was a bit curt with her on the phone. She describes that the front desk person sounded rushed, and also elaborates that if that was her perception, then she is concerned that patients may also feel hurried as well. This documentation can be added to the 360-degree review process along with team member and patient feedback gained from questionnaires. All of this input will elucidate a pattern of performance that the doctor alone would be unable to attain.

DOCTOR LEADERSHIP REVIEW

The doctor should also always be given an annual review. Yes, that's right. Doctors, perhaps more than other staff members, need constructive criticism, which they hardly ever receive. This type of doctor evaluation can be called the Dentist Leadership Review.

Most large healthcare entities solicit feedback on physicians from patients and staff. But such evaluations are just as important, if not more so, in small dental offices.

I will never forget attending my first meeting of dental office managers. When I called to register, I was told that I wouldn't be welcomed by the other attendees. I asked why, and was told that managers like to talk about their doctors. I went anyway. I was perhaps the only doctor in a large lecture hall of dental office managers. Judy Kay Mausolf was the speaker, and she was inquiring about office communication. The discussion included many areas of improvement for the doctor, including attendance at monthly team meetings (Yes, some dentists don't even want to attend their monthly team meeting!), lack of communication, and lack of respect for the team. I thought what a pity that other doctors were not there to hear this discussion! This information needs to be told directly to the doctors! This can be done by the team in the Dentist Leadership Review.

Personally, I have learned a lot from having an annual review from my team. First and foremost, it sends a message that their opinion of what I do counts. We're a team. I have been told to eat less garlic, brush my teeth after lunch, sit more gracefully, comb my hair more frequently, and of course, don't be late. All of these doctor self-improvements have been made due to the communication and honesty of my excellent team. Candor is essential.

A Dentist Leadership Review may include a review of skills and perspectives. These would include questions such as: Does the doctor manage the job challenges? Does the doctor lead people well? Does the doctor show respect for self and others? Does the doctor communicate effectively? Is the doctor's participation and attendance ideal?

Give the Dentist Leadership Review a try in your office. You will not regret it.

Part Seven

DISTRIBUTION OF RESOURCES

This is perhaps the world's greatest management principle:
You get what you reward.
– Anonymous

Verbal praise, as a form of reward, costs very little. Verbal praise can be given daily to both your team members and your patients who refer more patients. A financial raise may occur once per year, but a thank you, compliment, saying "well done," praise, or small gift card can motivate individual team members each and every day.

Performance is taken into consideration when deciding how HR resources should be distributed. Every day you have the opportunity to reward superstars, and discourage undesirable actions. Take time to analyze and assign rewards to the deserving areas of your office. Reward the behaviors you would like to see more of, discourage behaviors which need to be eliminated.

Wouldn't it be great if all of your team members came to work excited, fully engaged, and always giving their best effort? Having a highly engaged, capable, and active team is what HR management is all about. And even though you can't reach into someone's head and turn on their "get excited about your work" button, there are many things you can do to create a fun work environment.

Be careful not to reward low producers with less work and to punish highly productive employees with more work. This happens a lot in dentistry. A highly capable individual, especially at the front desk, is given more and more work until pushed to the brink of exhaustion, while low performers either do nothing to pitch in and help or are not given additional assignments due to their lack of capability. Remember to reward the superstars. Not everyone's work or talent is equal. Rewarding results promotes team fairness and builds individual effort and overall morale.

A visiting front desk temp once asked me, "How is it that all of your assistants can fit four second molar bands in twenty minutes?" I replied, "The schedule is the same for all of us. I would never hire or keep an assistant who could not place four molar bands in twenty minutes." This is the measure of ability, something that can be measured at a working interview. It also helps to have the assistant responsible for her own column of the schedule and to always know what time her patient's appointment ends. This will assure that the assistant stays on time.

When you ask great team members what motivates them, rarely is money their first answer. What is important to employees are often the intangibles, such as appreciation, opportunity to be heard, interesting work, an inspiring manager, great work environment, an empathetic boss, someone to listen to them, thoughtfulness, or being around people who care about them and about the patients.

In terms of dollars and cents, it's true that we don't get a bonus for trying hard. We don't get a raise every time the earth circles the sun. Financial rewards come from financial results. Financial success is what is monetarily rewarded in life.

Human Resource Management has a cost. Indeed, your office financial analysis may show that your employees may be your highest overhead cost. They are also your biggest asset and your best investment. They are stakeholders in your office. You want the most productive individuals for the price that you can afford to pay. You also want smart employees who are kind to your patients and who get along and work well together.

Productivity is something that you will need to constantly maintain. It is important for team members to realize that "trees don't grow to heaven"; there is a correlation to how much a doctor or team member can earn based on office collections. It is therefore a challenge for your dental office to have financial growth, with raises every single year of your entire career.

It is best to openly share the financial performance of the office monthly with the team as an incentive for salary increases and bonuses. Make your office success part of each member's personal success. Be transparent and work together on financial goals.

In order for team members to place their trust in the leadership, the doctor needs to make fiscally sound decisions that create sustainable employment. Team members then realize that it is their individual performance which contributes to the overall office outcome, which is directly responsible for their pay-rate and raises. It makes sense then to give pay raises after careful review of year-end collections. Pay raises may be separate from annual HR reviews, or if combined based upon the performance from the prior year.

In the orthodontic world, it has been stated that the ideal ratio of collections per hire is C/H = $200,000; or that total team compensation should be 20% of total collections. I met a dental practice consultant once who asked, "How many team members do you have?" Why not ask, "What is your HR overhead rate?" HR overhead can be anywhere from 0% (no employees) to 40% (the highest I have been recounted by my colleagues.) You may have an orthodontic office with twelve team members with 40% HR overhead or one with six and 20% HR overhead. HR costs reflect performance output. Every team member is different and every dental office is unique when it comes to HR overhead. There are several ways in which you can control HR costs.

1. Hire entry-level recent graduates for introductory positions. Train and promote seasoned talent from within your office. Make your office a place of growth and improve team member interest in learning all tasks. Continued promotion leads to increased longevity.
2. Hire part-time team members to work the busiest patient hours. Using this method, downtime is reduced. Part-time employees may include pre-dental students, high school interns, part-time working moms, or retired professionals looking to work only a few hours per day or week.
3. Maintain good team members. Training is expensive.

There are also financial considerations to the time spent in huddles, meetings, and advances. I would defend that this is time and expense well spent. However, even a 90-minute meeting with six workers will cost nine hours of production capacity. Considering the cost of a team meeting in this way: time must not be wasted. Don't eat lunch during this precious time but rather get down to serious business. For the best results possible, be sure to have everyone's thinking power and full attention. No cell phones, no boredom, and no lack of engagement. Everyone is involved, reporting, thinking, engaged, presenting new ideas, and a stakeholder. The office is the place of employment of everyone present and everyone present is responsible for the success of that office.

Chapter 20

FINANCIAL ANALYSIS OF HR

The secret of caring for your patients is
caring for your patients.
– Francis Peabody, M. D.

H R gold is the caring, thoughtful and respectful attitude of your
team toward patients. It is a cheerful service mentality. Look for
these attributes when hiring. Foster these habits on a daily basis. There
are financial costs of poor hiring decisions in terms of time, training, and
rehiring. There are the personal and emotional costs of HR issues.

When caring, thoughtfulness, and respect are absent, there is a tremendous cost to the dental practice. This cost could occur within the
practice walls or on social media. It could occur as negative word of
mouth in the community. Pay attention to what is being said, and how it
is being said in your dental office. Take care of whom you work with and
do business. Work with those who represent you well.

In this day and age, one negative comment made carelessly in the
dental office could end up posted by a thirteen-year-old patient on
Yelp. An assistant or business colleague could be using foul language on
social media. Supervise what is being posted or tweeted about your dental office as best you can. Distance yourself from behaviors that do not
reflect your values or the quality of your work.

There is great wealth to be gained by being emotionally controlled,
and interpersonally sensitive. There is a benefit to thinking before speak-

ing. There is wisdom in being mindful and calm under pressure. There is an infinite wealth in always being respectful to others, no matter what the circumstance. This applies to everyone in the dental office, especially the doctor.

CASE STUDY 42: "THE UNCIVIL DOCTOR"

Dr. Z's dental assistant was late for work and neglected to prepare the treatment room for the morning patient's procedure. In front of three patients, Dr. Z has an angry outburst. He publically ridicules and reprimands his dental assistant for being late and for not fulfilling her work duties.

Continuing to be emotionally upset and purposely aloof for the entire morning, Dr. Z cannot concentrate on his work. He does not complete his early morning patient's dental procedure with calm, ease, and finesse. There is tension in the room. The patient feels it and knows that something is wrong. The dental assistant who was admonished feels awkward. She appears nervous. She does nothing to reassure the patient about her dental procedure or to put the patient at ease. When the appointment has ended, the patient is escorted by the spurned dental assistant to the front desk. The dental assistant remains silent for the rest of the day.

The doctor continues to be angry all day. After lunch, he starts having chest pains. Sweat pours down his forehead. He wishes that this day had never happened. He hopes that the early morning patient won't have any additional problems with his procedure. Not feeling well, he leaves the room for a break and neglects to write up the patient chart for that day.

ACTION:
Doctors: don't sweat the small stuff. Forgive the little things and move on. A five-minute delay in room setup is nothing compared to the consequences of an unruly and uncivil workplace incident.

Dental assistants: apologize if you are late setting up a dental workspace for a procedure. Clear the air and put the doctor at ease. Make a point of acknowledging errors and stating that it will never happen again.

Everyone in dentistry: if you have an emotional outburst publically in the office, apologize immediately to all present. Don't hold a grudge. Never stay upset. Get back into your positive frame of mind by remembering that you are there in service to the patient. Smile and stay positive. Tell a joke! Remove tension from the air as quickly as possible. Move on successfully and enjoy the remainder of your day.

> *An apology is the superglue of life.*
> *It can repair just about anything.*
> – Lynn Johnston

What are the financial consequences to uncivil workplace behavior? Let's look at Case Study 42 once again from the patient's perspective.

The first patient, whose dental treatment is about to be done, may doubt the assistant's competence. She may think this individual deserves to be treated in a demeaning way because she is not a good assistant. She may feel the dentist's tension. She may witness his hands shake during the procedure or note that an instrument slipped. With her heightened powers of observation and feelings of doubt, she will certainly be attuned to any errors that occur.

Another patient in the same circumstance may compare this leader's relational skills to his clinical skills and begin to wonder if he is a good doctor. She may suddenly say that she is not feeling well and that she would like to cancel her appointment for the day.

A third patient might well wonder about the dental practice itself. Is she foolish to entrust her care to an office where patients are treated to a display of unprofessional behavior? She thinks, "What else could be wrong around here?" Her trust in the dental office is shaken. She decides not to ever return.

This is the high cost of uncivil workplace behavior. This is indeed the highest cost of poor HR management.

Chapter 21

BENEFITS

The worst mistake a boss can make
is not to say "well done."
— John Ashcroft

D epending upon the state of the economy and the financial success of the dental office, bonuses may ebb and flow. Benefits are not required by law. These workplace gifts are at the discretion of the practice owner. There are a vast variety of work rewards that a dental office may offer. Outlined below are the most common dental office workplace benefits.

VACATION DAYS

Vacations are essential, important for health, happiness and for work-life balance. We want everyone in office to enjoy their vacations and be able to relax. Most dental offices offer paid vacation days or paid time off (PTO). There may be a waiting period of one year to receive PTO benefits, after which one receives the initial paid vacation of usually one work-week time equivalent. The paid vacation days and benefits will follow the number of hours that the team member normally works per week. The maximum of three weeks paid vacation may be rewarded after five years.

Leave request

It is best for approval, communication, and documentation to place the vacation or leave request in writing. Team members should fill out a vacation request sheet at least eight weeks prior to the requested leave. This form includes a space where the team member will obtain the signature of the person who can cover for her during her absence. The doctor is the last to sign the vacation request after all arrangements have been made amongst teammates for coverage during the away period. The team member's chair or patient list for the day may be blocked during vacation so that the office is not shorthanded.

It is good practice, therefore, for the doctor to announce his or her own vacation time well in advance. Once school starts in the fall, our family tries to determine our vacation/conference time for the next 15 months or the entire next calendar year. This helps tremendously with off-time scheduling. Team members are always encouraged to take vacations during the time when the doctor is also away and the office is therefore closed to patients.

Paid Holidays

Your office can determine whether or not to pay for holiday leave. There is no law that requires payment for federal holidays. This benefit is at the total discretion of the dental office.

Many dental offices are closed on Mondays. This is a cost-savings measure for the office. With this office schedule, you might decide that the receptionist would be the only employee given a paid Monday holiday.

The federal holidays include:

New Year's Day, January 1
Birthday of Martin Luther King, Jr., Third Monday in January
President's Day, Third Monday in February
Memorial Day, Last Monday in May
Independence Day, July 4th
Labor Day, First Monday in September
Columbus Day, Second Monday in October
Veterans' Day, November 11th
Thanksgiving, Fourth Thursday in November
Christmas Day, December 25

The dental office may decide on which holidays the office will be closed, with either paid or unpaid leave. Of course, many dental practices may choose to be open on a Monday federal holiday since most patients and families will be off of work and available to come to their dental appointments. As an orthodontist, I have routinely worked on the Martin Luther King, Jr. holiday because "I have a dream." With kids off school and both parents available for their children's orthodontic examinations, working the Martin Luther King Jr. holiday has proven to be a very productive day.

DENTAL BENEFITS

In-office dental benefits may be given to employees. You may also wish to cover immediate family members. They may be given a percentage discount or perhaps simply be required to pay the supply and lab bill for services received. These benefits are viewed as less expensive for employees and also viewed as a convenience. In the delivery of dental benefits to employees, it is very important that the dentist keep complete dental records as for all dental patients regardless of whether the patient is also an employee. This includes the appointment of regular dental cleanings and recalls and documentation of proper referrals. It is also important that all dental procedures be supervised and at the discretion of the dentist, and that employees do not partake in procedures which could be considered "dental practice without a license" without the supervision or direction of the dentist.

Have a clear policy explaining the type of dental benefits that your dental office provides to employees and the limitations of the family members who are covered. Be sure to list those covered by the office dental employment benefit. You may want to include immediate family, such as a spouse, domestic partner, and children. You may want a percentage discount for parents and siblings. Be sure to include who is responsible for lab fees, when these appointments will take place, and your right to cancel this benefit at any time. Include the terms of the dental benefit in the Team Handbook.

Informed consent must be in writing, with a signed treatment plan for each employee and family member covered by the office dental benefit plan as it would be for any other dental patient of record.

Everyone who works in a dental office is a walking billboard for great teeth, fresh breath, and dental health that you provide. This is after all, our goal for each and every one of our dental patients and members of the general public. Promote dental health as a way of life by providing coverage for in-office care of your own team including the dentist.

RETIREMENT PLANS

ERISA (The Employee Retirement Income Security Act of 1974) rules establish fairness and nondiscrimination when distributing established pension and health plans in private industry to provide protection for individuals in these plans. A retirement plan benefit in the dental office will need to be established under the guidance of professional financial advisors. You will need an ERISA bond as insurance for the retirement plan. There is a fiduciary responsibility for those who manage and control plan assets protected by ERISA federal law.

Should you have a retirement plan in your dental office, you may want to require a vesting period of at least 1 year. To avoid administrative costs, you may even want to have a three-year waiting period for retirement plan participation. It is also prudent to stipulate that retirement savings be rolled over to a personal plan once an employee leaves. This will help reduce costs.

Retirement plans are an excellent work benefit but they have expensive administrative costs. Guarding and guiding the retirement-plan entry and exit will minimize expenses. Retirement plans include profit sharing, 401k employee contribution, and Safe Harbor employer contribution. An investment company or financial advisor will help you set up your office retirement plan. Administration of this program can be expensive, however, with minimum fees being on the order of $2,000 per year minimum. Retirement plans also pose a legal responsibility to the employer. ERISA requires that participants be provided with plan information, features and funding, and also sets minimum standards for participation.

UNIFORMS

Uniforms are a wonderful benefit to team members. Assistants love their office clothing especially if it is bright and cheerful. They spend hours looking through catalogs and can't wait to make new selections. This is one of the most popular perks that your office can provide. If you need a fresh pick-up of team morale, I suggest new office uniforms.

Uniforms indicate togetherness and pride, while showing off a clean and professional look. You want your team to be dressed for success. Providing wearables is one way to ensure a professional appearance standard. Uniforms can also offer a feeling of belonging and camaraderie.

Providing apparel is another way of branding your practice for patients, colleagues, and community. You only get one chance to make a first impression. Make that first look a good one!

Team members are asked to return their uniforms when they leave employment. In the state of California, the employer may charge for the cost of the uniforms and all unreturned items by deducting this amount from the final paycheck.

The only thing worse than training employees and losing them is to not train them and keep them.
– Zig Ziglar

Continuing Education

Most dentists pay for continuing education for courses that they would like their team to complete for the benefit of the office. Mandatory courses can be reimbursed by the doctor; voluntary courses should be paid by the employees themselves. In the state of California, two mandatory courses every dental team member must take are CPR and OSHA/California State Dental Law.

CPR courses are most commonly given in the office. Team members usually receive their hourly pay while learning CPR. OSHA and State Law can be attended locally or even taken by correspondence. Hourly wage is usually also given for the fulfillment of this course, which is also required for the doctor.

Team members may wish to attend a local, state, or a national association meeting for required CE units, or just for fun. It is not unusual for the doctor to pay for the registration as a gift or bonus. Should the team members attend a meeting that is registration-paid but hourly-unpaid, be sure to have documented that this meeting is voluntary, and that they will not be paid their customary wage for their attendance and travel time. It is important for each team member to understand that *the maintenance of the CE requirements for a license is an individual's responsibility.*

The dental office of employment is not responsible for CE requirements of individual team members.

Education fuels positive change. Invest in your team members' education to continue to build high clinical and service standards. Education will teach professionalism, verbal skills, and customer service, as well as keep everyone up to date on the continuous scientific advancements in the field of dentistry. Communication provided at CE courses eliminates apathy and misinformation. Local dental study clubs and societies are a great venue for continuing education.

Offices may also enlist in a variety of online continuing education through the American Dental Association (ADA), or the American Association of Orthodontists, AAO, or your local state and county dental societies, to name a few.

LUNCHTIME

All human beings love food. It's hard to resist Lunch-and-Learn meetings given by vendors. Keep them coming but make them voluntary. Have your team clock out. Otherwise, these meetings lead to an excessively high payroll and substantial and unnecessary overtime. Whether a Lunch-and-Learn is paid or unpaid, *be sure to still have your employees take a 30-minute break to clock out and physically leave the office,* so as to fulfill the law relating to mandatory break requirement.

TRAVEL

Each day, employees travel to and from work. Should work one day be at a new location due to CE or training, travel to this work, although further, is still considered the normal daily commute for employment. Travel to a meeting for such employment does not need to be paid by the office. Should parking or airline tickets be required, these are additional expenses and the office may choose to pay for these at their discretion. Very long-distance or overnight travel may be paid for at a different rate than the regular office pay rate. Have exceptional travel and work arrangements documents so that there is clear acceptance and understanding.

Holiday Parties

It is a joy to take time to celebrate. I often kid my team that someday when we are all in the nursing home together, we will still be remembering and talking about the year-end holiday party. These are great memories of happy times, which include funny stories, good jokes, delicious food, and mysterious limousine rides to and from our destination.

If off-site, limit alcohol consumption at your party to one glass per person for everyone's safety. The same rules of workplace harassment apply to the doctor and everyone from the office at holiday parties. To avoid trouble, be sure to maintain professional standards at all times.

Consider printing an invitation to your party that states what time the party starts and *what time the party officially ends*. When the party is done, call an official end. Clearly state "The party has ended. We are now done. You are on your own."

Holiday parties, year-end parties, and after-work gatherings are voluntary and unpaid. Should you pay your team to attend the holiday party, as an employer, you are now liable for all that goes on there including if someone were to be hurt, leading to a Workman's Comp claim.

If your party is an informal gathering after work or an impromptu social gathering, consider paying "Dutch" to remove liability.

Annual Bonus

My mother always taught me that money doesn't grow on trees. She was right! Bonuses are earned by the financial success of the office. An annual bonus may be given at the discretion of the office, based upon the revenue and profit of the office for that year. Bonuses may be based upon reaching a production goal, a collection goal, or both. Whether bonuses are equal or vary amongst team members, this decision is at the discretion of the practice owner or doctor.

To minimize tax deductions, it is possible to give bonuses in the form of a gift card. Please speak with your accountant to decide what is best for your bonus program.

Medical Benefits

The world of medical benefits is changing with the initiation of the Patient Protection and Affordable Care Act. Your office may have a group medical plan or your dental office may offer no medical insurance at all. Some dental offices have tax-free medical savings plans while others pay a set amount towards medical premiums. For each situation, the choice of medical benefits offered are still at the discretion of the dental office.

Part Eight

EMPLOYMENT LAW

No one is above the law.
– Anonymous

I n dentistry, the owner of a practice must function as CEO, CTO, CFO, COO, CIO, Director of Marketing, VP of Sales, Director of Product Quality Insurance, and HR Management Director. Most HR Directors in major corporations are full-time Attorneys and HR Specialists with advanced degrees and extensive training. Yet, the law treats dentists the same as the HR Director of a Fortune 500 Company. A dentist and dental office must abide by the same HR employment laws as Walmart, General Electric, or AT&T.

Live by the law and both you and your dental office will stay out of trouble. To follow the law, you must know the law. Employment laws deal mostly with the rights and fair treatment of employees. These laws deal with safety and non-discrimination. In order to maintain a lawful work environment, the law needs to be known, understood, and followed by dentists, dental office managers, and HR directors. Handled with finesse, implementation of these laws will create a safe, fair, and respectful work environment.

"All may dismiss their employee(s) at will, without thereby
being guilty of legal wrong."
– Payne v. Western and Arkansas
Railroad Company, 1894

EMPLOYMENT AT WILL, 1894

The Employment at Will doctrine is still one of the most important statements of present-day Team Handbooks. There is only one state which does not follow employment at will. That state is Montana.

Employment-At-Will describes that:

There may be termination of the employment agreement
by either the employer or employee
for any reason whatsoever.

While the Employment-At-Will doctrine has been extensively modified over the years, it remains in effect in many states. However, many other states now require that there be just cause (good reason) for the termination of employment. If no just cause exists, the practice can be held legally liable for the unjust termination.

Federal and state employment laws have been evolving for many years, creating more rights for employees. Regardless of whether you practice in a state that still recognizes Employment-At-Will, or one that requires just cause for termination, public policy prohibits all terminations for a "bad reason." ***There may <u>not</u> be termination for:***

1. *discrimination;*
2. *retaliation;*
3. *refusal to do an illegal act;*
4. *engaging in a protected activity;*
5. *demanding back pay or payment due.*

Laws and regulations frequently change. *Neither the information in this book nor any information found on the Internet should be a substituted for sound legal counsel.* Guidance should be sought from an attorney or HR professional in your state and locality with respect to specific statutes and regulations. HR Employment Law is a composite of federal, state, county, and municipal statutes and ordinances. Your local HR attorney or HR firm will know these laws best. Every dentist, office manager, and HR director would benefit from taking time to learn the Employment Laws which govern your dental office.

NATIONAL LABOR RELATIONS ACT (NLRA), 1935

We've all heard of dentists who have had their employees all walk out at once, most likely for some perceived injustice or adverse working condition. You may think that unions do not apply to dentists, but in many ways they do. This law states that *your team has the right to organize, form a union, bargain collectively, and engage in concerted activity for the purpose of mutual aid and protection.*

Fortunately, before dental employees walk out, they usually say, "We quit!" I've never heard of a dentist having a picket line out in front of their dental office. Most dental office handbooks have a statement saying that *should a team member abandon their job for any reason without just cause it is grounds for immediate termination.* In dentistry, when employees quit, we are often able to start hiring replacement employees that same day.

Many think that the NLRA, also known as the Wagner Act, applies only to those in a union. In fact, the rights granted under the NLRA apply to all workers, whether or not they are union members, and whether or not union-organizing activity has taken place.

Consider my true story. It was my first day working in the orthodontic faculty practice at a well-known dental school. On a Friday afternoon, the clock hit 5:00 p.m. While my last patient was still in the chair, I looked up to see all the dental assistants packing up to leave for the day. I asked, "Where's everyone going? I'm still here with my last patient." The response came, "We're in the union."

Out of the goodness of her heart, I had a very dedicated dental assistant stay with my last patient and me. She was within her legal right as a union member to leave. Fortunately she stayed. If she had wanted to leave, there was nothing I could have done about it.

Ninety-nine percent of dentists don't deal directly with unions. Even so, recognize the ability of your team to organize a collective action. Hire a team focused on patient care and dedicated to putting patients first as their top priority. In dentistry, we work in healthcare service, not a factory.

By definition, a *profession* literally means that a person professes, or takes an oath, to place the needs of others above their own needs. "Professional" is perhaps one of the most incorrectly and overused terms in society today. It is time for dentists and their teams to hearken back to the original, true meaning of "profession."

> *Help us girls...*
> *Today 200 of us have been cut down $6 to $4 dollars a week.*
> *A few months ago we were getting our minimum pay of $11 a week.*
> – A young girl to President Roosevelt,
> Bedford, Massachusetts

The Fair Labor Standards Act (FLSA), 1938

Most dental team members are paid by the hour. In choosing your starting wage for an entry-level job, even for a high school student, *you must pay minimum wage.* Each state has a minimum wage law. Municipalities may also have minimum wage rules. *Employers must display the minimum wage poster provided by the state, which contains the provisions of the FLSA.*

The FLSA is a national policy on minimum wages and overtime payment for "covered" or "non-exempt" employees. Check the labor standards in your state and municipality for the minimum wage. For example, in San Jose, California, the minimum wage mandated by the City Council ordinance is higher than other cities in Santa Clara County.

Overtime is generally considered to be 1 ½ times the regular rate for all hours worked over 40 hours in a work week. This stipulation is often part of fair labor standards in your state or municipality.

Employers must pay overtime at time and one-half the normal pay rate. In California, overtime is paid in excess of 8 hours in a day or 40 hours in a workweek. In most other states, overtime is calculated on a weekly basis only, so that employees qualify for overtime pay only if they work more than 40 hours in a weekly period. Employees are entitled to the maximum overtime pay afforded under federal, state, and municipal laws.

Non-exempt employees are those paid by the hour, who clock in and clock out. *Employers must keep all work time records for non-exempt* *employees.* To meet requirements in all states, records must be kept for a minimum of 4 years. These items include time cards, electronic time records, and other work documents. To be safe, it is best to keep work time records for seven (7) years or even longer. Digital records are even easier to save.

Exempt employees are usually paid on a salary basis and do not qualify for overtime; they are paid by the week, not by the hour. A high-level administrator, for example, may qualify to be an exempt employee. However, it is not their job title or method of pay that determines if they are an exempt employee. Rather, the employee must be acting in a supervisory capacity to be treated as an exempt employee and thus ineligible for overtime pay.

The doctor who owns the business is obviously an exempt employee. A full-time office manager who meets the qualifications of exempt status may also be salaried by the week and therefore exempt.

For administrative exempt status, three tests must be met:

1. The employee must be compensated on a *salary* basis at a rate not less than $455 per week.
2. The employee's primary duty must be managing business operations.
3. The employee's primary duty must include discretion and independent judgment with respect to matters of significance.

For more information, visit www.wagehour.dol.gov or call 1-866-4USWAGE. Please be aware that when state laws differ from the federal FLSA, an employer must comply with the standard most protective to the employee.

CASE STUDY 43: "THE EARLY RISER"

Rita was the full-time receptionist at a busy dental office. Rita liked to rise early to avoid rush-hour traffic on her way to work. This caused her to arrive two hours before the start of the patient day. She clocked in at 6:15 a.m. This resulted in ten hours of unauthorized overtime each week. At a regular pay of $20/hr. and at an overtime rate of $30/hr., this practice totaled an extra $300 dollars in HR costs per week. If left uncorrected by HR management, in a 50-week work year, this would lead to a staggering $15,000 in overtime pay for Rita per year.

ACTION:

If someone wishes to enter the office early to avoid traffic, allow them to do so, but stipulate that they not sign in until fifteen minutes before the start of the workday. Every office manual should have a clear policy regarding overtime and preauthorization for additional hours. It is prudent to have a policy that employees clock in no sooner than 15 minutes before the start of their work duties.

Consider putting all non-exempt employees on notice that overtime must be pre-authorized as written in the Team Handbook. If the employees fail to gain this approval, abuse of overtime can be grounds for termination, in accordance with the office policies.

With the "Early Riser" or her twin sister the "Late Leaver," it is important to verify that they actually were physically in the office early (or late) at the times claimed. Simple manipulation of the computer time clock is also a possibility. Verify with your alarm system company that your office alarm was indeed turned off in the early morning hours (clock-in) or set in the late evening hours (clock-out) as reflected in the employment time card. If you prefer not to have an old-fashioned locked time-stamp card machine to track hours worked, then mandate that an Internet clock be used. By contrast, clocks in desktop computers or many computer management systems can be easily altered to falsify the time.

Nursing mothers also have the right to take breaks to pump breast milk in the workplace under a provision of the FLSA national policy. The FLSA is enforced by the U.S. Department of Labor's Wage and Hour Division. See www.dol.gov for more details.

PORTAL-TO-PORTAL ACT, 1947 (FLSA AMENDMENT)

This law defines the parameter of what is considered employment. Here, work preparatory and concluding activities, waiting time, meals and breaks, travel time, and training time are considered.

If attendance at lectures, meetings, training programs is considered **mandatory** for work, then payment must be given for hours attended. If the event is outside of normal work hours and considered **voluntary** and not related directly to the practice of dentistry, compensation need not be provided. It is important to clarify, in writing, what is mandatory and paid and what is voluntary and unpaid for all continuing education courses, team development activities, outings, and events.

Rest periods or break periods of 20 minutes or less are customarily paid as working time. Meal periods of 30 minutes minimum are not paid and need to be clocked out after a maximum of five hours worked. The employee must be completely relieved from all job duties while eating to be unpaid.

An employee is generally paid for making drop-offs for the employer, even if it is on the employee's way to or from work. If the chore is an indispensable part of the employee's job activity and solely for the benefit of the employer, time is compensable. This applies to delivery of patient dental records, gifts, or other documents to other offices or locations in the community. It is important to avoid off-site activities as much as possible in order to minimize other liabilities associated with travel.

> *Since President Kennedy signed the Equal Pay Act in 1963,*
> *the gap between men and women's earning*
> *has narrowed by less than a half cent per year.*
> *At this rate, American women will have to wait until 2062*
> *to bring home the same salary as their male counterparts.*
> – Jackie Speier

EQUAL PAY ACT (EPA), 1963

This law prohibits sex-based compensation discrimination. It is fair to have equal pay in equal jobs that require equal skill, effort, and responsibility, performed under similar working conditions, within one establishment. *Pay men and women the same.* Modifications are based on seniority and merit, or the quantity/quality of work.

PREGNANCY DISCRIMINATION ACT OF 1978 (PDA) (TITLE VII AMENDMENT)

Do not ask the question "Are you pregnant?" at the initial job interview. Do not discriminate on the basis of pregnancy, childbirth, and related medical conditions. Pregnancy is to be treated as any other short-term disability. If due cause exists to fire an employee who is pregnant, make sure to be extra careful in documentation and warnings of poor work performance.

The PDA forbids discrimination based on pregnancy. This applies to hiring, firing, pay, job assignments, promotions, layoff, training, and fringe benefits, such as leave and health insurance. The employers may need to supply modified or light duty, alternative assignments, disability leave, or unpaid leave.

A pregnant employee is to be treated just as any other temporarily disabled employee. Impairments from pregnancy such as gestational diabetes or preeclampsia may be disabilities under the Americans with Disabilities Act (ADA).

When I was pregnant, I realized just how difficult it was to work in dentistry, on our feet all day in this condition. My shoe size went from a size 7 to a size 10. When my sister, an internal medicine physician was pregnant and working, she had to rest on an exam table during lunch each day to improve leg circulation. When necessary, such accommodations need to be made without discrimination or harassment.

CIVIL RIGHTS ACT OF 1964 (TITLE VII)

Title VII describes *the prohibition of discrimination in compensation or work conditions on the basis of gender, nationality, religion, color, or race.* This applies to all private employers with employees of 15 or more, with respect to hiring, training, appraisals and promoting. Title VII is especially important when applying disciplinary action or terminating an employee.

CIVIL RIGHTS ACT OF 1991 (TITLE VII AMENDMENT)

This law codifies remedies for proven discrimination. The possible out-of-pocket obligations for the employer for the employee include the compensation for such things as finding a new job and emotional distress. *If an employee prevails in court, the employer may be required to pay the employee for lost wages, lost promotions, mental anguish, legal fees, and court costs.* The judge may also require the employee to be reinstated. If the employer acted with malice or reckless indifference, the court may award additional punitive damages.

AMERICANS WITH DISABILITIES ACT (ADA), 1990; ADA AMENDMENT ACT (ADAAA), 2008

The ADA law tells us, *"Do not discriminate on the basis of physical or mental disabilities."* A disabled person is one who has a limitation in one or more major life activities, including caring for self, walking, seeing, hearing, speaking, working, sitting, standing, lifting, sleeping, thinking or concentrating, and interacting with others.

CASE STUDY 44: "THE TALENTED LIBRARIAN"

The fifth of five children born at home to a Polish immigrant worker at a mill, Anastasia was the first child to survive. The trauma of the birth caused oxygen deprivation, resulting in cerebral palsy and broken bones.

Anastasia did not walk until she was four years old. As a child, she needed crutches to go to school. Her speech was labored. Manual dexterity was strained, and she wrote slowly but beautifully.

Despite her outward appearance and physical limitations, Anastasia had a very sharp mind. She continued to improve her manual skills by knitting. She improved her overall muscle strength by working in her family's farm garden. Eventually, the crutches were discarded. She graduated from high school and went to college.

There, Anastasia first achieved a Bachelor of Science in chemistry. She tried working in a hospital lab. Her manual dexterity was a limitation for this job. Then she obtained additional training to become a school teacher. Physically, this job was too physically demanding for her as well. Finally, she decided to obtain a Master of Science degree in a less strenuous profession. She chose to pursue library science and become a librarian. After years of struggle, education, and soul searching, Anastasia finally had her first long-term job as a librarian at a major university. She was now forty years old.

For the next thirty years, Anastasia excelled as a librarian. She continued to be promoted until she became the top librarian at the university. She built a new home and lived alone. She was put in charge of a famous archive in the school and given an executive office on the top floor of the library. She became one of the highest paid employees at the university. Eventually, she was asked if the library could be named in her honor.

ACTION:

The Americans with Disabilities Act (ADA) protects qualified individuals from discrimination on the basis of disability. Disabled adults deserve an equal opportunity to work.

The ADA requires reasonable accommodation of disabled persons to perform essential job functions unless it creates undue hardship. Accommodation may include modified work schedules, reassignment, alteration of equipment or devices, and changes of training and policies. Quality standards need not be lowered as a consequence of the accommodation. All ADA requests from applicants and employees must be considered. The employer is not required to appoint the disabled person to a new job that does not already exist.

Temporary, non-chronic conditions are not disabilities. Pregnancy is not considered a disability. With technological and other medical advances to help people with disabilities being invented and developed every day, this area of the law changes quickly. Please check with an HR attorney for more details.

The Americans with Disabilities Act applies to all employers with 15 or more employees or greater. If you have five employees or less including the doctor, almost none of the ADA applies to your dental office.

Age Discrimination in Employment Act (ADEA), 1967

Do not discriminate on the basis of age, especially in those over age forty (40). This applies to hiring, training, appraisals, promotions, disciplinary action, or termination. ADEA covers private employers with 20 or more employees. Remedies can include consideration for loss of retirement benefits. Failure to comply can be very costly.

The Bona Fide Occupational Qualifications Law allows for mandatory retirement ages for certain occupations and highly paid employees and executives. While ADEA prohibits discrimination against older employees, it does allow companies to set a mandatory retirement age, recognizing that physical abilities diminish with age.

The Civil Rights Act of 1964, Americans with Disabilities Act (ADA) and the Age Discrimination in Employment Act (ADEA) all prohibit discrimination in every aspect of employment, including pay, job assignment, benefits, and any other term or condition of employment.

*Preventing employment discrimination from occurring in the first place
is preferable to remedying the consequences of discrimination.*
– EEOC

Equal Employment Opportunity Commission (EEOC), 1965

The laws of employment are enforced by the EEOC, a federal agency. It works to prevent discrimination. Its job is enforcing *FAIRNESS* in the workplace. *The employee must file charges within 180 days of the alleged discriminatory action, or 300 days in states that have a fair employment practice law and state agency.* The employer has the opportunity to respond to the charge. The EEOC can bring a direct suit against a company if they believe that there is a pattern of discrimination. This suit would be filed in federal court.

Posting Requirements

Employers are required to post notices describing the state and federal laws prohibiting job discrimination. The EEOC's poster is available at www.eeoc.gov. State posters are also available.

*Some of you may know my story:
How for nineteen years, I worked as a manager
for a tire plant in Alabama.
And some of you may have lived a similar story:
After nearly two decades of hard, proud work,
I found out that I was making significantly less money
than the men who were doing the same work as me.*
– Lilly Ledbetter

Lilly Ledbetter Fair Pay Act, 2009

The Lilly Ledbetter Fair Pay Act of 2009 was signed by President Obama on January 29, 2009 with an effective date of May 28, 2007. This act extends the time period in which employees can pursue disparate pay claims under four anti-discrimination laws: Title VII, ADEA, ADA, and the Rehabilitation Act (Rehab Act.) Amendments to the Equal Pay Act (EPA) provide for uncapped compensatory and punitive damages for violators.

Who was Lilly Ledbetter? Lilly worked at Goodyear Tire and Rubber Company. She retired in 1998 and then sued the company for paying her significantly less than her male counterparts. The lawsuit reached the Supreme Court but was denied because she didn't file her claim within 180 days from her first paycheck.

United States Supreme Court Justice Ruth Bader Ginsburg wrote: "Over time, Ledbetter's pay slipped in comparison to the pay of her male counterparts. By 1997, Ledbetter was the only woman working as an area manager. The pay discrepancy between Ledbetter and her 15 male counterparts was stark: Ledbetter was paid $3,727 per month; the lowest paid male received $4,286; the highest paid was $5,236." The Ledbetter case also pointed out that pay disparity further leads to inequity in overtime pay, contributory retirement, 401(k), and Social Security savings.

A discriminatory paycheck is considered a wrong that is actionable. Under the act, the timeliness requirements for the filing of a discrimination suit are loosened, as long as it reflects a past act of discrimination which occurs within the 180-day period of limitations. A discriminatory pay decision, which starts the 180/300-day period to file a charge, occurs each time a discriminatory paycheck is issued. With this act, the EEOC (Equal Employment Opportunity Commission) announced it would place more emphasis on enforcement against pay discrimination. When "a person" is affected by a discriminatory compensation decision, even a spouse of a deceased worker may claim that pension benefits have been reduced by a discriminatory decision. This law further prohibits discrimination against older workers.

IMMIGRATION REFORM & CONTROL ACT (IRCA)
Fines may be imposed on employers for recordkeeping violations. *Within three days of hiring, the new employee and the employer must complete the Form I-9.* This form verifies both identity and the employee's right to work in the United States. *Employers are required to maintain the I-9 form for a minimum of three years after the date of hire and for one*

year after termination of employment. U.S. Government officials, such as the Department of Homeland Security or Department of Justice use this form in their monitoring of individuals in the U.S.

Employers who knowingly hire someone who is in the U.S. illegally may face civil and criminal penalties. Yet, in the state of California, one may not ask at an interview, "Are you a U.S. citizen?" Instead, you may ask, "After employment, will you be able to provide work documents?" This puts the burden of discharge on the employer.

The E-Verify Internet-based system allows employers to check on the eligibility of employees working in the U.S. Employers submit information taken from the new hire's I-9 form to determine if the data matches the federal records. Government contractors must use E-Verify. Certain states have mandated its use. Many employers use it with good intent. It can be found at www.uscis.gov.

IRCA prohibits discrimination against job applicants on the basis of national origin and citizenship. It also establishes penalties for hiring individuals who do not have the legal right to work in the United States. It is applicable to all employers with one (1) or more employees.

We have now reviewed several employment laws applicable to dentistry. Fear not, we are halfway through. To summarize, the Big Four which you need to know to stay out of employment law trouble are: ADEA, ADA, EPA, and PDA. By now, I hope that you have gotten the admonition that *to be lawful, do not discriminate.*

> *These men ask for just the same thing,*
> *fairness, and fairness only.*
> *This, so far as in my power, they, and all others, shall have.*
> – Abraham Lincoln

FAIR CREDIT REPORTING ACT (FCRA), 1970

Employers must obtain authorization before obtaining consumer reports for applicants or present employees. In addition to providing a summary of FCRA rights, employers must disclose the report and afford the individual an opportunity to correct errors in the report. *Employers who request reports, such as credit scores, must receive the consent and cooperation of applicants and/or employees.*

In the state of California, it is now illegal to run a credit report on applicants or present team members, even if these individuals will be handling money. Please check employment laws in your state or verify with your local attorney or HR specialist.

Employee Retirement Income Security Act (ERISA), 1974

This federal law sets the minimum standards for voluntarily established pension and health plans in private industry to provide protection for individuals in these plans. ERISA requires that employers provide participants with plan information about features and funding. It also sets minimum standards for participation, vesting, benefit accrual and funding. *Employers have a fiduciary responsibility to protect retirement plan assets of their employees.*

ERISA gives participants the right to sue for benefits owed and breaches of fiduciary responsibility. If a defined benefit plan is terminated, participants are guaranteed payment of benefits through a federally charted corporation, the Pension Benefit Guaranty Corporation (PBGC).

Fair and Accurate Credit Transactions Act (FACT), 2003

This law is an amendment to FCRA. It provides reversal of the need for consent and disclosure requirements **in the event that the investigation involves suspected workplace misconduct or violation of a law, regulation, or employer policy.** *Employers with suspected workplace violations of the law, policy, or misconduct, may hire a third-party investigation of workplace issues without first notifying the individual(s) being investigated and gaining consent.*

The FACT Act is the only federal law that specifically requires employers to take reasonable measures to reduce the risk of identity theft to their employees. In general, *an employer who obtains employee information as part of a background check must use reasonable measures to dispose of the information in such a way that no one can gain unauthorized access to it.* This usually means shredding documents or making computerized data unusable before disposing of it.

CONSUMER CREDIT PROTECTION ACT (CCPA), 1968

The CCPA protects employees from being terminated due to wage withholding for bad debt. It also limits the amount of money that can be taken in any one-week period. *An employer may not discharge an employee because of garnishment of wages for indebtedness.* Court orders or other legal or equitable procedures requiring wages to be garnished could include debt to the Internal Revenue Service (IRS), or to a state tax collection agency. Visit www.dol.gov for more information.

EMPLOYEE POLYGRAPH PROTECTION ACT (EPPA), 1988

Have you sometimes wondered if your employee really had twelve family funerals on twelve Fridays in a row? Have you ever wanted to give an employee a polygraph test to confirm or disprove a worrisome action? Well, you can't. *It is unlawful for private employers to use a polygraph or "lie detectors" in pre-employment screening or during the course of employment.*

A polygraph is permitted for certain high-security jobs. These would include positions such as bank guard, alarm serviceman, or driver of an armored car. In polygraph-approved jobs, employers are required to display the EPPA poster in the workplace for their employees.

In rare cases of suspected involvement in a workplace incident of theft, embezzlement, or injury to an employer, an employer may, under strict conduct of licensed and bonded testing, give the polygraph to an employee. The Act limits the disclosure of information obtained during such a test.

You may feel that you would like to do some screening of potential new hires, present employees, or those with suspect activities which may warrant termination. Be sure that these checks are done legally with consent. To help you complete these tasks properly, consider HireRight services. They can be found at www.hireright.com. They offer over 100+ unique screening services, including background checks, I-9, drug and health screening, and check of public records.

RETALIATION

Individuals "covered" against retaliation include those employees who declared their opposition to potentially unlawful practices of discrimination based on race, color, sex, religion, national origin, age, or disability.

Protected activities include filing claims of discrimination, refusing to obey an order thought to be discriminatory, or complaining about discrimination. *An employer may not fire, demote, harass, or otherwise "retaliate" against any employee for filing a charge of discrimination or participating in any proceeding against the doctor or dental office.*

Retaliation occurs when an employer takes an adverse action against an employee. Refusal to hire, denial of promotion, and termination may be viewed as adverse actions. Individuals in close association with these employees are also covered and protected by this law.

EMPLOYEE COMMUTING FLEXIBILITY ACT, 1996
Should the dental office give the employee a car, or use of a car, then the Employee Commuting Flexibility Act would apply. *In order for commuting time not to be considered hours worked, the employee must be within the normal commuting area and the use of the vehicle agreed upon between the employer and the employee.*

GENETIC INFORMATION NONDISCRIMINATION ACT OF (GINA), 2008
This law states that all medical and genetic information must be kept in strict confidence. The best practice is to keep this data in a not-accessible place with strict and secure access. *Do not discriminate based on medical records revealing genetic information.* Genetic medical information cannot be disclosed. The law prohibits insurers from charging higher premiums based on genetic information in underwriting decisions. This law also applies to employers with 15 or more employees.

THE FAMILY AND MEDICAL LEAVE ACT (FMLA), 1993
This law applies to public agencies and private businesses with over fifty (50) employees, which is rare in dental offices. FMLA leave may be leave for their own serious health condition, for the birth of a child, for adoption of a child, for foster care of a child, for a spouse, child, or parent who has a serious health condition, or for the bereavement of immediate family members. As an example, *employees are allowed to take 12 workweeks of unpaid, job-protected leave per year that may be used to care*

for the new child. The employee must have worked for the employer for 12 months prior to taking the leave.

This law protects jobs during times of absenteeism for serious illness and maintains group health benefits. The FMLA, which is enforced by the U.S. Department of Labor, allows employees to balance work and family responsibilities by taking reasonable unpaid leave for certain family and medical reasons. For more information see www.dol.gov.

Health Insurance Portability and Accountability Act (HIPAA), 1996

The HIPAA law as it applies to employees is designed to provide protection to the confidentiality and security of their personal health data as stored in their private personnel file. The HIPAA privacy rules protect the employees. *Employers may not disclose unauthorized personally identified health information (PHI).* The confidentiality that HIPAA provides for employees makes it easier for them to change jobs and become insured with new employers, without discrimination or breaks in their medical coverage. In addition, employers must train all of their employees in privacy rule requirements for themselves and for their patients. Employers also must not use PHI for making employment or benefits decisions, for marketing, or for fundraising.

If you have additional questions regarding how HIPAA in the dental office applies to both employees and patients contact Tom Terry, Dental Seminars. He can be reached at tom@tomterryseminars.com.

The Affordable Care Act, 2013

The Affordable Care Act presents a new "Patient's Bill of Rights." It states that health plans can no longer limit or deny benefits to children under 19 due to a pre-existing condition. It also extends young adult coverage under parents' health plans until age 26. This law removed the insurer's ability to cancel medical insurance coverage for preexisting conditions and gave patients a right to appeal for denial of payment. With the Affordable Care Act, if you have 50 or fewer employees, you can purchase affordable health insurance through the Small Business Health Options Program (SHOP).

The Affordable Care Act banned all new health insurance plans from having a lifetime limit on medical coverage. It also requires all medical insurance companies to publicly justify any unreasonable rate hikes and required a decrease in administrative costs. The focus of care is preventive at no cost or co-payment to the patient. The Affordable Care Act also opens emergency care at hospitals outside of network.

For more information on the Affordable Care Act visit www.HHS.gov/healthcare.

Employment laws affect HR management in the dental office. Don't be an employment law fugitive! When it comes to HRM and law issues, play it safe and seek legal counsel.

For more information on employment law, visit these useful Internet sites: U.S. Department of Labor: www.dol.gov, EEOC: www.eeoc.gov, and similar employment sites in your state.

Chapter 22

TERMINATION

Breaking up is hard to do.
– Neil Sedaka

There are many reasons why team members leave their place of employment. Young individuals may leave for a career change, a less demanding job, for additional education, to get married, move away, or to stay home to care for young children. Middle-aged team members may leave for career change or family commitments, including caring for elderly parents. Long-term team workers may get burned out, need a break, take early retirement, or have personal or family obligations. Occasionally, there is someone that you just have to terminate whose leave is not voluntary. No matter what the circumstances, make it a goal to part on good terms. Put as much thought and effort into a team member's leaving as you do into their hiring. Ease and love departing team members out the door. No matter what the circumstances, make it a goal to separate as graciously as possible.

Voluntary Leave
To a boss, the words "I quit" may come as a surprise. This emotional, knee-jerk reaction of resignation, whenever spoken, should be taken seriously. Ask the person to write down their resignation on a piece of paper and date it before walking out the door. You don't want to foster a

"cry wolf" employment behavior in your dental office.

If a valued member plans to leave under good terms, giving two weeks' written notice of voluntary termination, you may request that they stay on longer to help select and train their replacement. This can be helpful, especially if they held an important job and are not easy to replace. If it is a highly skilled position of responsibility, you may want to request and need more time for the transition, perhaps up to one month to interview, select, and train the new hire.

If the team member is not a positive contributor to the team, you may want to dismiss them immediately once they have given the "I quit" notice. It may not be beneficial to keep the team member in the office, especially if they are going to be telling every dental patient, in an unfavorable tone, that they are leaving or giving information that they are going to work in another office across town or down the street. If you dismiss them immediately without additional hours or pay, their resignation date and time is the final day of their term in your office. From that date and time, their final paycheck and separate vacation paycheck will be written. Be sure to record the date and time on their resignation notice.

Whenever a valuable team member quits, ask them their reason. Gain their opinion of your office work environment by asking for feedback. If they are changing jobs because of the presence of a toxic team member who is driving them and potentially other co-workers crazy, you need to know this. If there are working conditions which could be improved for the better, you need to know that as well. These and other questions can be asked on a questionnaire to be submitted during the final exit interview.

> *Executives owe it to the organization and to their fellow workers*
> *not to tolerate nonperforming individuals in important jobs.*
> – Peter Drucker

Involuntary Leave

Involuntary leave includes being laid off, being "let go," becoming redundant, or being fired. Whatever the situation, it is not a pleasant one and needs to be handled with planning, skill, sensitivity, and finesse.

Layoff

During the recession of 2008, layoffs from dental offices were common. As an employer during challenging financial times, the decision to lay off one or two team members may be a better choice than cutting the salaries or hours of the entire dental team. Personally, I'd rather have a smaller, 100% happy team then a larger 75% not-quite-as-happy team.

Pay cuts, hourly cuts, or time cuts can make team members unhappy and less enthusiastic about their jobs. Be judicious about your layoff strategy. Analyze, document, and prepare. Complete annual reviews and make known the financial downturn weeks or months before the layoff. Rank all employees on a scale of 1-10 in several areas. Lay off the lowest performers. Laying off one or more than one team member, if necessary, may ease the pain. Keep a record of why these particular team members were laid off, just in case this information needs to be presented or reviewed in the future.

Once the layoff is complete, be sure to have a team meeting to rally your remaining troops, "the survivors," and let them know that you remain committed to them. Take time to talk about it to clear the air. This is perhaps the most important thing of all.

> *There is only one boss, the customer.*
> *He can fire everybody in the company from the chairman on down,*
> *simply by spending his money*
> *somewhere else.*
> – Sam Walton

Firing

If you think breaking up is hard to do, try firing someone. Letting someone go will be the most difficult and awkward situation that an employer or HR manager will ever have to face. You own this decision. You made a mistake hiring this individual, training this individual, coaching this individual, and now you are responsible for making their departure as gentle as possible. Handle firing with extreme care.

The dental office and doctor will be most at risk of legal ramifications when someone is fired. Claims of bias or partiality are not uncommon. The dental office may find itself in the position of defending the judgment of the person who did the firing, whether it is the doctor, the office manager, or HR coordinator.

In situations of imminent firing, it would be beneficial to collect multiple office perspectives, if for no other reason than to show that the resultant verdict is the product of a jury-like system. The probability that multiple people rating independently share a biased or discriminatory attitude is very low. The 360-Degree Reviews offer not only deeper perspective on evaluation of team members, but they are also a safeguard in the decision-making process by demonstrating fairness of multiple opinions.

I have been very fortunate in my career to never have needed to fire someone. Maintaining a philosophy of "keeping the pressure on" underperformers and communicating expectations, I have found that team members either rise to an acceptable level of performance, or voluntarily quit. When held to a performance standard, low achievers fire themselves. With open communication, if improvement is deemed impossible and firing is inevitable, give the team member the opportunity to resign. This is a win-win face-saving situation for both the employee and the employer.

Termination is a serious action that generally is the culmination of a series of progressive disciplinary actions. Be sure to have documentation of coaching in an effort to help the employee improve. Have warnings in place.

Legal causes for termination include:

Violation of code of conduct
Failure to follow policy
Violence or threat of violence
Insubordination
Harassment
Watching pornography online

When terminating, remember that team members have personal lives and families. Being fired can decimate an individual on a personal level and diminish their professional self-esteem. While you, the dentist or HR manager, want to be kind, you need to understand that disruptive bad behavior or lack of innate ability often cannot be changed. The frustration of both parties can go on for years. Although termination is a difficult task, leadership must act to do what is best for the dental patients, office, and team. A doctor who suffers with a difficult team member, suffers at his or her own peril.

WRONGFUL TERMINATION

For a dismissal to be determined to be a wrongful termination, the dismissal must violate a specific law, statute, regulation or constitutional provision. If an employee complains about something which is legally owed to them by law, such as overtime, and they are fired, this is wrongful termination. Should there be discrimination of any type within the dental office with dismissal, this would also be wrongful termination. Whistle-blowing by an employee for illegal activity of the employer or refusal to do something which is illegal would also be considered wrongful termination. Not allowing an employee to perform a lawful duty such as jury duty or retaliatory termination for asserting rights would also be found to be wrongful termination.

EXIT CHECKLIST AND FINAL PAY

No matter the type of termination, preparations need to be made and completed. They are listed below:

1. Final paycheck hard copy
2. Vacation paycheck hard copy, separate
3. Final paycheck acknowledgement form
4. Resignation letter signed and dated
5. Type of resignation documented
6. Return of company property checklist
7. 401K rollover information
8. Exit interview
9. Termination documents acknowledgement

For more information regarding the final paycheck and final vacation pay, visit www.dol.gov/dol/topic/wages/lastpaycheck.htm.

EXIT INTERVIEW

At the end of the employment cycle is the exit interview. This process provides the practice the opportunity to learn what the departing team member liked and disliked about their job. It gives the owner valuable insight into what could be improved for future HR management. It is an excellent opportunity to thank the team member, learn new things, or just clear the air. Most people who leave possess useful knowledge and experience; exit interviews provide direct indications as how to improve the work experience and to increase retention rates.

A feedback questionnaire form may be given once you have received notice that a team member is leaving. This will give the person time to think about the questions and prepare their answers at home. These forms may be returned at the time of the final day, face-to-face exit interview or mailed back should the employee wish to not return to the office.

In the best situation, office owners will receive constructive feedback and the employee will leave on a positive note, with good relations and mutual respect. In the worst situation, the employer may want to wait a few weeks, let emotions settle, and mail the exit interview form for feedback. Time allows employees to gain perspective. They still may be able to offer some constructive criticism from which the dental office may benefit.

Some exit interview questions can include:

Why have you decided to leave?
Was a single event responsible for your decision to leave?
What did you value most about working at our office?
What did you dislike about working at our office?
What are your views about the management and leadership at our office?
How would you describe the culture or "feel" of our office?
Could you offer comments on how we could improve?
Is there any other problem which you would like to discuss today?

Give the departing team member this final open-ended question and let them talk. If nothing else, it will clear the air and help end the relationship on a positive note. It has been reported that fifty percent of OSHA claims to the Dental Board resulting in an OSHA inspector visit to the dental office were instigated by employee retaliation for dismissal.

Avoid blaming a departing team member for a situation. Remember to always treat people with respect and integrity. Pay attention to whatever facts you may learn at the exit interview and take action when necessary to improve your office and your office teamwork. Thank the departing employee for their work in your office and be grateful for the time you had together. This will be appreciated by all and a relief to the keepers left behind.

Chapter 23

UNEMPLOYMENT BENEFITS

*The Great Depression,
like most other periods of severe unemployment,
was produced by government mismanagement
rather than by any inherent instability of the private economy.*
– Milton Friedman

A *former employee can collect unemployment benefits when he or she is
terminated for reasons other than gross misconduct.* In the event that a
terminated employee files for unemployment benefits, you must provide
written documentation of the employee's gross misconduct to the unemployment office. If the terminated employee challenges the gross misconduct, a hearing will be scheduled to determine the matter. Usually,
the doctor and/or office manager may be required to testify at such a
hearing.

State-run unemployment insurance is a program that pays approximately 60 percent of a person's pay for usually 26 weeks (6 months). The
purpose of unemployment insurance is to help people who lose their job
to survive financially while looking for another job. This program can be
expensive for the former employer. The company's rate is determined
by how many claims were payable to former employees of that company
made in the last year.

*Employees terminated for gross misconduct are not entitled to unemploy-
ment benefits.* Depending on state laws, gross misconduct may include:

Absent without notice
Theft
Harassment
Falsification of company records
Fights or threats of violence
Insubordination

Unemployment insurance cannot be collected if the employee quits voluntarily. If a claim is filed, you may submit any documentary evidence of "quitting" to the unemployment office so that benefits will not be issued. When an employee quits, therefore, it is important that you request to *receive the resignation in writing.* Alternatively, you can document the resignation and have it signed by a witness. Some attorneys feel that "it is a cold day in California for someone not to get unemployment benefits." Your documentation of the resignation in writing is critical for your office not to pay unnecessary unemployment benefits.

CASE STUDY 45: "The Quitter"

One day, Francesca told her dentist, "I quit." She had decided to move to a new community. The dentist requested that Linda write on a piece of paper, her name, the date, time, and the statement: "I, Francesca Neverlast, voluntarily resign from my job at Such and Such Dental Office on Today's Date, Time, Signed, Francesca Neverlast"

Francesca handed this written statement to the doctor who in turn signed it and dated it "Received Such and Such a Date and Time." The doctor handed the document to the HR manager who also signed and dated it. The resignation was placed into Francesca's personnel file.

Two weeks later the dentist received a request for unemployment benefits from City A to be paid for Francesca. The dentist called the unemployment office and informed the officer that Francesca voluntarily quit her job. He faxed the signed document. Unemployment benefits were denied.

Four weeks later, Francesca filed for unemployment benefits again, this time in a different office and city, Town B. The dentist called the second unemployment office to tell the officer that Francesca voluntarily quit. He faxed over the signed document. Unemployment benefits were denied for a second time. Perhaps Francesca finally understood that she could not collect unemployment benefits after voluntarily quitting her job.

ACTION:

Be sure to have the voluntary leave statement written, signed, and dated at the time of resignation. If for some reason the team member will not put their resignation on paper, write it for them and have them sign it. If they refuse to sign it, or leave the office before it can be signed, write a resignation account yourself and have a witness sign it. Further documentation can be achieved by typing "voluntary separation" in the memo line of the final pay and vacation checks, whilst keeping a copy of these checks in the personnel file. These simple actions and documents can save your business from unnecessary unemployment charges and expenses in the future.

A recent study of BambooHR found that 31% of people have quit a job within the first six months of employment. That's a high percentage, one out of three. Here are the top five reasons U.S. workers in this study gave for leaving new jobs:

1. Changed their mind on work type desired (career path)
2. Work was different than expected
3. Boss was a "jerk" (tyrant)
4. Didn't receive training
5. Job wasn't fun

It is always a goal to keep turnover low and minimize unemployment benefit costs. We can't do much about the first two answers above as to the why people leave employment, or the individual wants, needs, and fulfillment of our employees, but we do have the ability to be a great boss, train and coach our employees, and keep the office fun. These actions, in the end, should keep turnover at an ideal rate.

Chapter 24

GIVING REFERENCES

A good face they say,
is a letter of recommendation.
O Nature, Nature,
why are thou so dishonest,
as ever to send men with these false recommendations
into the World!
– Henry Fielding

When team members leave employment at your office for any number of reasons, you will have to decide what to say to other employers who call for a reference. Over the years, you will be asked to give references for great, good, and not-so-good departed team members. It is recommended by attorneys that the dentist make it an office policy to provide the following information:

1. Date of hire;
2. Position held;
3. Duties performed;
4. Response to a document asking to *verify* a specific rate of pay that you will either confirm or deny;
5. Date of separation.

If possible, say nothing else or very little more about the departed team member. Good or bad, whatever you say can be used against you. By following the steps above, you will be protected.

In the state of California, it is illegal for an employer to give misleading information whether good or bad regarding a former employee. Imagine that you as the doctor give a glowing written reference to a former employee who performed great in your office. She then goes to the next office, embezzles, destroys their computer system, or blows up their nitrous oxide tank, burning down the office. If you gave a good reference, especially in writing, there is potential liability that you gave a false reference for an employee who was in some way not in fact satisfactory. Perhaps you sugarcoated the abilities of the former employee or were untruthful about the facts of her employment or the weaknesses in her personal work capabilities.

On the contrary, an employee who you may have fired for lack of accountability in completing tasks may have matured from her experience, learned an important life lesson, become more motivated, and is looking for a second chance at work. Giving a bad reference is fuel for potential retaliation. The last thing you want to be involved with is libel (written) or defamation (verbal) attack of character leading to an employee lawsuit. Damages could be awarded to the former employee for suffering or other financial loss.

Have an office policy not to give written references. Have this reference policy written in the Team Handbook. Inform everyone on the team and be clear about it in advance. Also, have noted who will be answering the office reference calls. In most offices, that would be the doctor.

Verbal calls for references will come into your office asking about former employees and interns. Believe it or not, these reference calls are rather few. From my own personal experience over the past twenty-five years, I have found that most dentists actually don't take the time to make a personal job reference phone call to their colleague to ask about departed team members they are considering for hire. This oversight may indicate total confidence in the new hire. Or, it may mean inattention to a sound hiring process. By not calling to ask about references, a dentist could overlook a potential new hire threat. Once hired, the dentist and team will now suffer needlessly at their own peril that which they could have avoided should they have hired a toxic person without a good reference.

A Good Reference

If an employee was maintained for several years, this is a positive sign. When the new HR manager calls for a reference, they will hear in the voice of the dentist how delighted the former employer was with the candidate. The new employer will most likely ask, "What is the documented departure reason?" This can be easily answered by "moved away" "quit" "resigned" or "laid off due to economic downturn." The HR manager may ask, "Company policies aside, would you rehire this candidate?" You could answer pleasantly without reservation. A favorable review will be confirmed by the doctor's attitude and tone of voice in giving a good reference.

A Truthful Reference

There is always a temptation to cover up bad news with a sugarcoating. When necessary, avoid this temptation. Silence speaks louder than words. Be silent when you are not able to give a good or positive reference.

Imagine you had a dental assistant who was violent in the workplace or even threatened a coworker. You may choose to only giving name, rank, and dates of employment, but don't try to hide the unacceptable workplace behavior by speaking unnecessarily about other good things. Don't lie about it. You may find yourself in legal trouble for failing to warn the new employer about the serious problems of the candidate when they resurface again at the next job. Have a truthful reaction regarding performance facts.

A Negative Reference

When it comes to difficult employees who have left your office, it is the best policy to say as little as possible and always stick to facts that you have documented in the former employee's personnel file related to job performance. If the former employee was less favorable or "terminated," if called for a reference you will face a difficult situation. Proving that an employee stole, lied about job qualifications, or is incompetent may be difficult. If you make such a statement about a former employee and the employee does not get the next job, it could get you into trouble should a revengeful employee file a defamation lawsuit stating that you are the reason they cannot find employment or stating that you have discriminated against them.

You can avoid such problems in the first place by telling a difficult employee the obvious: "I cannot provide a positive reference for you." If possible, do this before they leave employment at your office. In this way, hopefully they will not list you as a reference. In the state of California, the previous employer can refuse to provide information beyond the general employment dates and position held.

Part Nine

_____

LEADERSHIP

You are not a leader to win a popularity contest.
You are a leader to lead.
– Jack Welch

A few years ago, I set up an unofficial local dental-office management study club in my local community. After posting our meeting
on Facebook, a dental supply rep showed up at my office asking if she
could sponsor the food for our meetings. Yes! We were delighted! Next,
a regional dental supply manager showed up at my office to view my
business book library. She declared "I'm sending you to a national dental
management meeting, paying your registration, and giving you an all-ex-
pense paid trip!" I could not believe my ears or my good fortune! All I
could say was "Wow!" There certainly is return on investment (ROI)
with Facebook!

With anticipation for what would happen next, I imagined Peter
Drucker's *Management by Objectives* being discussed at this meeting or
Jack Welch's *Sigma Six Principles* being applied to dental team manage-
ment. Perhaps Tom Peters himself would be there *In Search of Excellence*!

The meeting started with an outstanding performance of Adele's
song "Fire." I thought it was the real Adele singing! The fun never ended.
It felt like one big party. Gathered were a lot of interesting people in
dentistry. Indeed, this is where I first met Fred Joyal, a great guy and co-
founder of 1-800-Dentist, who wrote the foreword for my first book, *It
All Starts with Marketing*.

At this meeting, I was very impressed with the dental office managers who had completed an online CE program in dental management and received fellowships awards in a concluding ceremony. After this meeting, I decided that I would delegate more responsibility to my own Office Manager and Assistant Office Manager and enroll them in the online dental-management fellowship process.

This meeting ended with a five-member panel discussion by dental coaches for the benefit of dental office managers in the audience. Here, participants could ask any question from the audience floor to the dental-consultant experts on stage. I sat in the audience with several dental office managers at a round table. I sensed by our table group discussion that each dental manager was thinking the same exact question, *"Can I lead and implement change in my dental office and still be part of the team?"*

Suddenly, someone asked what everyone was thinking, *"Will the dental office manager ever truly be part of the dental team?"* There was a nervous hush in the ballroom. All present squirmed in their seats. The consultants dug deep for their answers. Then, like a beacon of light on a dark stormy night the answer rang true with clarity from dental consultant Amy Kirsch, who courageously and truthfully stated, *"The dental office manager cannot truly be part of the team. She was hired to be something else. The dental office manager is a liaison between the doctor and the team. She was hired to lead."*

> *Leadership is not something done to people,*
> *like fixing your teeth.*
> *Leadership is unlocking people's*
> *potential to become better.*
> – Bill Bradley

Organizations need both management and leadership for optimal effectiveness. Professor John Kotter of the Harvard Business School describes management as coping with complexity. Good management brings about order. This order could come in the form of education, organization, implementation, planning, changing, and leading.

In dentistry, practice management often deals with the day-to-day challenges of running a business. Often we deal with human-performance issues. Good managers bring about order, fairness, and consistency. They handle the details of HR execution well. HRM is an extremely important job. It needs to be clearly understood, and responsibility taken for getting the task done. Once in place through leadership, clear HR management will bring peace to your dental office, especially for the doctor.

Leadership is about change. The doctor is the ultimate leader, leading the team. Leaders have a vision, mission, and goals to achieve. Leaders align people towards fulfilling their vision and inspire the team to overcome hurdles along the way.

The office manager and HR director are also leaders in the dental office. They need to clearly understand the mission and goals of the office and be in full communication with the doctor. In some dental offices, there may not be an official dental office manager. The doctor there must lead alone, day-by-day, with on-the-job training. Leadership requires action supported by courage, communication, and candor.

It is critically important that "the tail does not wag the dog." The doctor or dental office manager leads, makes decisions, sets a vision, enforces core values, and takes responsibility. They are not to be swayed or set off course by rebuttals, setbacks, resistance, or difficulties along the way. The leader sets the goals and direction for the team. The leader has the biggest influence on office culture.

Employee problems are essentially management problems and it is up to management to solve them. Take responsibility and get things under control. Otherwise, you could end up with a "the tail wagging the dog" situation. Don't let the tail wag your dog! The day you do is the day that you abdicate leadership in your office.

The dental office is a human community, like a living organism. The leader tends to the dental office as one tends a garden. Day by day, the actions of tending the garden need to be strategic. Living organisms evolve. Flowers grow, but so do weeds. Fruit trees need to be pruned. Weeds need to be removed. The tending of your dental office organization never ends.

Seven Types of Leaders

In their book, *Essentials of Organizational Behavior*, Professors Stephen P. Robbins and Timothy A. Judge assess contingency theories of leadership by their level of support. Leaders are described as either being transactional, exchanging rewards for actions, or transformational, instilling internal motivation and values. Described here, in order from least effective to most effective, are seven types of leaders. Which one are you? How could you change to be better?

Laissez-faire

The laissez-faire leader abdicates responsibilities and avoids making decisions. Perhaps their response to daily challenges is "Ask the office manager" or "Ask the consultant." This gives all rights to the team members. They have no leadership. Employees must make their own decisions and act on their own.

Laissez-faire leadership is often described as being "hands off." The leader, most often the doctor, may not even be present at office meetings, if there are any meetings at all. This is the most passive of all leadership and management styles.

Outside experts, such as team specialists or consultants are often being used when laissez-faire leadership exists. In this situation, employees need to have self-motivated pride in their work and the drive to do it successfully, on their own, without external guidance.

Management by Exception

Leaders in these dental offices maintain the status quo. They tend to be available and engaged only when there is a problem. This is what we call "Crisis management." In this type of leadership, feedback and availability are often too late. Intervention comes only if rules have been broken or standards are not met.

Contingent Reward

Here leaders start to take an active role in the motivation of their team. They offer rewards for effort. Good performance is recognized in materialistic or psychological form by money or praise. There could be a bonus system by which performance is recognized financially. Accomplishments are noted. The constant feedback emotionally supports continued performance.

With Contingent and Management by Exception leadership, leadership starts to become effective. The transactions of both of these Transactional Leadership styles have benefits. These management styles promote performance, but they will not get team members to go above and beyond the call of duty to the highest level of performance excellence.

TRANSFORMATIONAL LEADERSHIP

Transformational leaders inspire team members in the dental office to transcend their own self-interests for the good of the patients and the practice. The four major categories and characteristics of transformation leadership are Individualized Consideration, Intellectual Stimulation, Inspirational Motivation, and Idealized Influence. These styles of leadership produce outstanding results.

These leaders are capable of having an extraordinary effect on their employees. By challenging and inspiring, they give them a sense of purpose and excitement about daily work. This form of leadership motivates team members, and gives them a vision of what is possible and what they can aspire to in building the dental office of their dreams.

INDIVIDUALIZED CONSIDERATION

The Individualized Consideration leader instills pride in each team member. The vision and mission are clearly stated, accepted, and implemented. The openness of communication builds respect and trust. As a result, there is extra work effort from individuals, with higher productivity, improved morale and satisfaction, and enhanced organizational effectiveness.

These leaders have a low absenteeism rate, as individuals are devoted and care about the work that they do. Individual consideration is applied by verbal thanks and praise, public recognition for work well done, and frequent congratulatory reinforcements. Individualized consideration includes career counseling, education, and mentoring.

INTELLECTUAL STIMULATION

The Intellectual Stimulation leader creates an environment conducive to the creation and sharing of knowledge. This leader acknowledges that assistants are incredibly smart and capable of learning many things. With this comes the understanding that each team member wants to continue their professional and personal growth. They want to read informative books about their work. Like dentists, they want to attend meetings, learn, and implement new ideas, and give their own presentations.

This leader challenges individual team members to become champions of their own personal development and office responsibilities. Individual ideas are openly expressed and brainstorming encouraged. Great new ideas are implemented for the good of the office. In turn, team members are proud of their contributions, have intellectual fulfillment, are satisfied, and in turn highly motivated to act rationally to solve office problems for the good of the patients. *They see it, they own it, and they resolve it.*

INSPIRATIONAL MOTIVATION

The Inspirational Motivation leader uses symbols to focus and inspire efforts. They offer a clear and appealing view of the future. Through motivational conversations and displays of optimism and enthusiasm, they raise everyone's imagination regarding positive outcomes to work towards.

An Inspirational leader is often heard saying "Let's GO!" and "We can do this, together." An Inspirational leader constantly expresses high expectations and the important purpose of the organization. They stimulate teamwork and appeal to each person's inborn desire to attain high goals of love, learning, and leaving a legacy. They motivate team members to make the world a better place.

IDEALIZED INFLUENCE

The highest level of leadership and effectiveness is Idealized Influence. With this type of leader, the office goals are clearly explained and reviewed in a charismatic manner. The vision is compelling and team members are excited to be part of it. The mission is understood, accepted, internalized, and expressed by all. The mission values the importance of the contributions of each team member, who understands how his or her own individual work is part of the fulfillment of the larger purpose.

Idealized Influence is leadership by example. These doctors display a high level of ethical and moral conduct. They act confidently and optimistically. Trust exists through vulnerability and sharing risks and results with the team. The followers admire the leader as a role model, and there is an organizational closeness. The team shares many group experiences gained through frequent meetings and outings. Members respect themselves, their teammates, and the leader.

With the Idealized Influence leader, individuals have personal pride in their work and they are self-motivated to serve the patients. Team members are invested as stakeholders in the success of the dental enterprise.

In the new economy, HR management and dental office leadership have produced leaner and flatter organizations to maintain profitability. With fewer employees, strong and clear leadership is more critical than ever for the effectiveness of the team and the success of the dental office.

> *True compassion means not only feeling another's pain*
> *but also being moved to help relieve it.*
> – Daniel Goleman

CASE STUDY 46: "THE EMPATHIC LEADER"

Jennifer was not herself at work. Her father had been placed on hospice for a terminal illness. She would frequently burst into tears and she was unable to concentrate on her work or give patients the full attention that they deserved. She was physically and emotionally exhausted from taking care of her dad in the evenings.

Everyone including the doctor was concerned for Jennifer. She had gone from being a high performer to a low performer. She was also the office manager and a seventeen-year veteran at the office. She had gone from being the strongest team member to the weakest team member overnight.

ACTION:
The doctor made the decision that Jennifer should take family leave until her home situation had resolved. Jennifer was happy with this decision. The assistant office manager who had been cross-trained for the manager position seamlessly took over temporarily. Jennifer continued to come into the office occasionally for a few weeks and contributed to important tasks.

A few weeks later after the passing of her father, Jennifer returned to the office. She was emotionally and physically strong again and happy, and her performance was once again excellent. It was good to have her back.

Every team member has their own family and works for their reasons, not yours. They have feelings and they are human beings. Every person is special. Everyone will have a personal situation someday which will be a challenge to their work. It is important as the leader to recognize when something is wrong with an individual and find a solution.

The leader and HR manager must ask, "Who is this person at work?" "What is their performance?" "What is their special situation?" Special situations are infrequent. They are not consistent events. It is important to know your team members well enough to be able to recognize these times.

Leaders must be close enough to relate to others,
but far enough ahead to motivate them.
– John Maxwell

Leaders inspire teams. Your job as the leader is to evaluate, coach, and build self-confidence in your members. Dental team members are not like golfers, keeping their own independent score as they go through the course of the day. The dental office team is more like a baseball team. Working together, each person needs to "play their position" throughout the day in order to "score the run": obtain a new patient referral and start the dental treatment.

Leaders need to make sure their team sees the vision and lives the core values of the dental office. Your job as a leader is to keep people on track and remind them of the office goals and mission. Leaders also need to exude positive energy and intelligent optimism.

A leader models and shapes ethical behavior. This includes integrity. The tone and example at the top pervades the organization and either inspires the team to act ethically or it does not. Leaders have the greatest influence on the team because they are the distributors of rewards and punishments, carrots and sticks. To be a leader with integrity, tell the truth and keep your word. Take responsibility for the actions of the team, admit mistakes, and fix problems. Play by the rules, which are kept fair for everyone.

Leaders, by the way they create, enforce, model, and interpret team policies as written in the Team Handbook, influence their team, who in turn, treats the patients and creates the office culture and work environment. Ethical leadership is associated with more positive work behaviors. This is a wake-up call to dentists about the importance of modeling their behavior to the dental team members who look up to them.

Leaders need curiosity to probe into office systems to get answers about how things are being run. They need to ask: "What happened?" and "Why?" In bad times, leaders take responsibility for what has gone wrong and they fix it. Every problem has a solution and it is the leader's job to put the solution in place.

The leader of HR will need to make some tough decisions. They may need to correct an employee, document problem behaviors and even terminate. But one thing is for sure, they are not there to win a popularity contest.

As the leader of HR, you are there to bring out the best in your team, and to make your dental office the absolute best that it can be. At times, you will have an "uh-oh" feeling about situations. Listen to this intuition. Your conscience, or your "gut instinct," knows when a situation is not right. It knows when the parts of the story don't add up. This uncertainty nags at you. When this occurs, dig deeper into the problem. Ask more questions. Investigate the situation. Then, face the facts.

After all the hard work of leadership and HR management, leaders need to celebrate with their team. Once things are in place, let go and let the team do their excellent work. Once achieving success, the praise goes to the team for a job well done. For a happy work environment, it's important to take time to recognize and celebrate the team's achievements. After winning the World Series, it's time to uncork the bottles of champagne!

Chapter 25

TEAMWORK

*Teamwork remains the
ultimate competitive advantage.*
– Patrick Lencioni

It is the goal of HR management to make the dental office the best that it can possibly be. Time and attention are needed to build a high-performance team. Investing time in alignment and teamwork is like tuning a fine engine. It creates efficiency that will not only pay in results, it will make the whole journey of your dental office success smoother and more fun.

A doctor cannot run a successful dental office alone. Building the ideal team is not a quick fix. It requires daily attention, communication, systems, and time. It is necessary to observe teamwork, review teamwork, grade teamwork, and reward teamwork. It is not about a group hug, or singing "Kumbaya." Teamwork is first communicated as a goal, learnt, felt, remembered, understood, and finally acted out.

What do you do when rules are broken? Do you point out goals are not being achieved? Do you allow someone to break up the team? These are times for teambuilding and individual and teamwork assessments. These assessments are made of individuals because the weakest link may pull down the entire team. Make sure that everyone on your team is a strong link who is willing to work together for overall success.

In our office we spell teamwork TO CARE. These letters stand for Trust, Ownership, Communication, Accountability, Results, and Excellence. These are characteristics we select for and develop in each team member. We call our employees "team members" because we are indeed a team. We function and work together efficiently and effectively to achieve common goals.

TRUST

Few things can help an individual more
than to place responsibility on him,
and let him know that you trust him.
– Booker T. Washington

How does a leader, dentist, or HR manager build trust? It's simple. Trust is candor and transparency. It's keeping your word. It's accepting and fulfilling responsibility. It's giving credit where credit is due.

Trust is a two-way street. You need to trust your team for them to trust you. Trust is the glue that holds the team together. Would anyone on your team say, "I'm not sure that I can trust this person?" If so, maybe that person needs to go. Members of trusting teams admit weaknesses and mistakes, ask for help, give help, provide feedback and assistance, offer and accept apologies, and look forward to working together.

Exercises to discover and build trust may include open discussions about personal histories. Questions could include number of siblings, hometown, unique challenges of childhood, favorite hobbies and interests, first job, worst job, and individual challenges. Revealed by these histories are our vulnerability and humanity. This knowledge enables individuals to bond with each of us and to develop close relationships and deep understanding. This is the essence of why time spent together out of the office is extremely important. Sharing these moments builds team trust.

To build teamwork effectiveness, ask each team member to identify their personal contribution to the team as well as one area of improvement for the good of the team. Team members can be asked, "What is one thing that each person could do to improve the team?" These action items can be discussed openly in a team setting. Try it. It could be some of the best feedback your team will ever receive!

242

Tell the truth,
the whole truth,
and nothing but the truth.
— Oath of the U.S. Justice System

A team honor code states that members will not lie, cheat, steal, or tolerate those who do. Without trust, you are committed to *"snoopervision"* in an attempt to double-check everything that an untrustworthy team member does. This is a tense situation. It's that feeling of "walking on eggshells" or having "an elephant in the room."

Trust is perhaps the most important characteristic of a functional team. When vulnerability-based trust is present, everyone is free to say "I screwed up," "I need help," "Your idea is better than mine," "I wish I could learn to do that as well as you do it" and "I'm sorry." When this level of honesty is present, trust will then be an office culture.

Trust produces security and leads to individual team member empowerment. Conflicts diminish trust. In order to have a trusting team, *everyone must get along.* This is a crucial goal of leadership. It will require the courage, communication, and candor of leaders to address and maintain positive team dynamics at all times. Never ever, for the sake of peace and quiet, allow conflicts to continue so that trust is diminished.

OWNERSHIP

Job ownership is an attitude of
excellence, achievement and expertise.
— Walter Sasiadek

Ownership of the job with commitment to follow through on what needs to be done is one of the most important things that you need to look for in a new hire. Devotion to ownership is evident on day one, as reflected in the resume. Here the signs say either, *"When I start something, I finish it,"* or *"I fail to finish what I start."*

Team members need to make the commitment of being stakeholders or "owners" in their dental office. They do this through their actions of speaking positively and openly about the office, and by communicating all concerns and plans for improvement.

The measure of ownership is action. Job owners are motivated to be stars. They work harder and longer to receive results. They jump into new challenges with a willingness to learn. They take full responsibility for the results of their work and don't let things fall through the cracks. Take time to explain and foster the attitude of job ownership with your team by communicating that it is what you expect. Pause to reward job ownership actions and behaviors. Those who work longer and harder to produce ownership results deserve reward and recognition.

The opposite of ownership is apathy. This is the TGIF attitude which leads to no performance or poor performance. Reject the statement, "I'm busy." This is the response of a team member watching from the sidelines. If you hear this ask, "Busy doing what?" Team members can never be too busy when it comes to patient care or customer service. Instill ownership, understanding, and motivation. Spell out expectations of involvement as clearly as possible. Make each team member know how important he or she is to the overall team effort and goals of the team.

It's not enough to delegate or to give an assignment. Team members need to have the desire to get the job done. Each person commits to clinical excellence, outstanding customer service, and delivering a great patient experience, following through by their actions. Have each team member buy into your core values and mission. They can take pride in how their individual efforts make a difference in driving the dental office and team forward.

COMMUNICATION

It is only by friction that we polish.
– Mary Parker Follett

Mary Parker Follett (1868-1933) was an American social worker, management consultant and pioneer in the fields of organizational theory and organization behavior. In 1898, she graduated from Radcliffe College, but she was denied a doctorate at Harvard on the grounds that she was a woman. She was one of the first women invited to address the London School of Economics and she was a consultant to President Theodore Roosevelt. She is regarded by some as the "mother" of Modern Management for speaking on "cutting-edge" issues.

Peter Drucker called her the "prophet of management" and his "guru." Her cutting-edge-issues included "reciprocal relationships," "integration," and "power with" rather than "power over." She coined the phrase "win-win philosophy" in her work with groups. Her approach to conflict was to embrace it as an opportunity to develop integrated solutions rather than to compromise.

Perhaps the mother of HR, Mary Parker Follett was a champion of the "soft" factors of management. In management, she advocated for a human-relations emphasis which contrasted with the "scientific management" of Frederick W. Taylor, which stressed time and motion. She looked at leadership holistically and she stressed the interactions of management with workers in "informal processes," the first and foremost of these being "communication." Her book *Dynamic Administration* (1942) was published posthumously.

Evaluate your own office communication. Do you take time *each day* to meet, talk, and review how everyone is working together? Analyze, "How are we doing?" "How do we talk to one another?" and "How do we listen?" Listening is more than 50% of communication.

Communication can be taught, practiced and reviewed. One team rule of communication is that only the truth can be spoken. Whether right or wrong, we need to talk about situations that need improvement. This way, corrections can be made immediately. Should a change need to be made, help can be found, and jobs can be rearranged—*we can work it out.*

We're back at the Morning Huddle. A huddle is a time of communication. Possibilities are morning huddles, noonday huddles, after-work huddles, monthly huddles, retreats and advances, reviews, and one-on-one sessions. Open communication is included in all of these. Any opportunity to look each other in the eye and say what's on your mind and in your heart is time well spent. Be sure to be open to the suggestions of others and to listen.

One forum of communication is the monthly team meeting. For an effective meeting, be organized, have an agenda, discuss areas where improvement is needed, and assign individual responsibility. Brainstorm and set goals while giving everyone ample time to talk. Follow up on meeting action items, and evaluate project outcomes.

Think about how important it is to bring to light the areas of improvement for your dental office. This is most difficult, as people are embarrassed and shy about what needs to be addressed and done, especially if it involves their area of the office. You may be thinking, "How can I tell her?" regarding an individual behavior. Try thinking, "How can I *not* tell her?" For the sake of the team and what is best for the office, candor prevails.

Communication is admitting what is wrong. You can't fix what you don't know is broken. With open communication, meetings will be lively, team members will be engaged, and problems will be resolved quickly. There will be friction. This too shall pass quickly as what needs to be improved gets completed.

Signs of lack of communication include the responses "I'm too busy," "I'm doing something," "I don't care," "I just won't say anything," and "I don't know." These are not acceptable responses for open communication.

For effective team communication and effectiveness, sentences using *I* and *me* should be eliminated and replaced with *we* and *together*. The leader can focus on pronouns such as "our, we, and us." *We are all equal and important. We are all working together. Together we will achieve this.* Teamwork is maintained through effective communication.

Make teamwork communication a top priority. You may want to try a buddy system. If one person is late, we are all late; if one person is absent, we are all absent. If someone is missing, we call. If we do something as an office, we all participate. Don't make exceptions. We're a team.

Remind people that it is impossible to read each other's minds and feelings. If you need something expressed or accomplished, say it or write it down. Be proactive with communication. Pay attention to verbal trends in your office.

CASE STUDY 47: "THE MIND READER"

Dr. Blue complained to his dental colleague Dr. Pink that his front desk assistant never delivered the daily mail to the mailbox across the street. Dr. Pink asked him, "Did you ever ask your front desk person to do that? Did you ever ask her to desert her desk, ignore your patients, turn her back on her teammates, leave the building, and avoid being hit by a car while putting the mail in the mailbox across the street?"

Dr. Blue explained, "I shouldn't have to ask her to put the mail in the mailbox across the street. My front desk assistant should just know on her own that it needs to be done and just do it!"

Dr. Pink replied, "Your front desk receptionist cannot read your mind. How can she know what you want done and when you want it done if you do not express this to her? Ask her to deliver the mail across the street to the mailbox at 10:00 a.m. each morning before the mail truck comes. Communicate this to her and also put it in writing. See what happens."

Dr. Blue did this. He communicated precisely by descriptive means the exact action that he expected and required for ideal job performance. He also set a time of day when he would like this task done. Dr. Blue's front desk assistant has been depositing the mail in the mailbox across the street every day ever since.

ACTION:

Ask and you shall receive. We cannot read each other's minds.

I am amazed at the power of communication and with being as precise as possible when asking for specific tasks to be completed in the office. Communicating and rewarding the tasks which you wish to be completed as part of your daily office schedule ensures their permanence even further.

After reading Bruce Tulgan's book, *It's O.K. to Be the Boss,* I learned the lesson of precision communication more clearly. For months, I had been asking a team member to gather email addresses for all patients of record in our office. This was a large task that needed to be done for every patient in our database, going back nearly twenty years to the start of our practice. My front desk receptionist had been working on this project, gathering a few email addresses every day. I couldn't help but think, "At a rate of one dozen email addresses each day, this job will never get done."

Then, I implemented Bruce Tulgan's advice of getting very specific in my work request. I stated, "Today is Thursday. Tomorrow the office will be closed to patients and you will have adequate time to gather email addresses. By Monday I need 1,000 additional email addresses."

When Monday morning came, I was amazed and pleasantly surprised when my front desk assistant stated, "Dr. Gorczyca, I have acquired 1,209 additional email addresses!" I couldn't believe it! It was amazing! Be specific. See what happens.

It only takes one minute to refocus your team. Communicate clearly what is most important for each team member to focus on accomplishing for the day. If necessary, try using the word "FOCUS!" Take time to concentrate every day on the few important things that need to get done.

An outstanding communicator is Mike Kryzewski, "Coach K," longtime head of the Duke University's Men's Basketball Team and the Olympic Men's Basketball "Dream Team." During times of disengagement, teamwork struggle, or lack of focus, I often think, "What would Coach K say?" The scenario would go something like this:

"O. K., Time out. Everyone huddle. It's your choice. You can either help me or you can do it alone. Here's the plan. Your head has got to be in the game! *Put your head in the game! FOCUS!!!*" Try talking like Coach K once in a while. Your team will quickly get the point, of concentrating on the task at hand.

Teamwork is not just being present every day, or showing up. Don't be afraid to address lack of engagement. Motivation and engagement are about being at work, always at your best. Engagement can be assessed by simply asking, "What are you doing right now?" and listening for the response. Engaged team members are doing things for patients, the office, or the doctor, or having an office project that they are working on. If the response is "I'm thinking about my boyfriend," this person may need to refocus.

To give North Carolina fans equal representation, here's how the legendary coach of the University of North Carolina Men's Basketball Team, Roy Williams, would address lack of engagement. Roy would say something like the following:

"Make a decision. Want to be part of this team? If so, do something. Be part of the team! I am not going to allow you to just go through the motions."

Dental office communication is the mirror of the doctor's attitude and engagement. From everyone in the dental office, we want a "Yes!" attitude. This is one of enthusiasm, service, gratitude, and teamwork. We want all to come to work each day and say, "Great patient opportunities today. I am so excited, happy, and grateful to be here!"

Maintain your positive communication. People do better work and put forth greater effort under a spirit of approval than under a spirit of criticism. Use positive language like, "Good morning!" "How may I assist you?" "I'll be happy to!" "My pleasure!" "Thank you!" "I appreciate that!" "You're welcome!" For the doctor, it is important to communicate, "I believe in you," and "Job well done," as often as possible.

Use positive body language. Avoid negative signs such as crossed arms and rolling eyes. Listen between the lines. Enthusiastic comments are great but complaints will give you more information on how you can improve your office. When you hear the response, "Fine" or no response at all, start asking more questions.

ACCOUNTABILITY

Accountability breeds response-ability.
– Stephen Covey

With a small team in the dental office, everyone counts and every action matters. With a close-knit working group, there's no place to hide. There is no way to be other than accountable.

The absence of one working individual in the dental office may in some cases double the workload for another vital team member. Therefore, everyone's presence and full participation is of the utmost importance. Working together is critical and each team member is needed for getting the day's tasks done.

The doctor alone cannot complete all of the tasks of the dental office. Together the small dental team is carefully integrated to produce the daily common goals. One goal may be a certain number of new patients or case starts per month. Announce the goal. Agree on the goal number. Let everyone know the goal and review the goal weekly. Make sure that office activities and behaviors of each team member are in line with this specific goal.

Maintaining a high level of performance in the workplace is not easy. It will require discussing accountability with underperforming team members in an effort to inspire and coach improvement. Continue to publically praise and reward those team members and actions which show accountability for a job well done. Accountability is self-discipline with respect for authority, personal responsibility, and honesty. Each team member is responsible for his or her social behavior, maturity and emotional intelligence at work. These are all factors of accountability.

Attitude and social development are reviewed on a child's kindergarten report card. "Exhibits a positive attitude, shows respect for others, socializes at appropriate times, interacts positively with peers, displays self-discipline, and accepts responsibility for their own actions" are all evaluated in a six-year-old. If this can be asked and graded for a kinder-gartener, it certainly can and must be asked for and maintained by your dental team members!

RESULTS

Some of us will do our jobs well
and some will not,
but we will all be judged on one thing: the result.
– Vince Lombardi

Huddle: "How many patient referrals have we received this month? Who made the phone calls back to new patients? How many new appointments have we booked?" However you measure the results, your metrics will need to be monitored on a daily, monthly, and annual basis for the maximum performance of your dental team.

Results need to be made known to maintain a competitive edge. It is not OK for a newly evaluated patient to leave and start treatment in another office. Expect to book the dental treatment for every new patient exam. Ask for customer service feedback. Report on new patients every day. This is your dental team score.

A lack of commitment to office results is apathy. This problem is often revealed by statements such as, "I will *try* to do it," or "I'll get to that" or "I'm busy." Preferred answers for result questions are "Yes," or "No." There are no "passing the buck" answers given by a results-oriented team.

Every team member needs to be contributing to the results of the office. If someone is out sick and the overall function improves, take this as a very good indicator that this individual is not contributing to the team and may even be pulling the team down.

If you are not creating, making, or selling our products,
you had better have a good reason for being here.
– Senior executive, PepsiCo

Ultimately, it is the results of the dental office that produce the HR benefits and sustain employment. Success is a collective achievement. No one, not even the doctor, produces all the results alone. It is a team effort. Results are the goals of the team.

Every sports team has a score. Every dental office has a score as well. Your monthly production and collection numbers are clear scores. There is no ambiguity here. Share these numbers with your team. Write your ideal score down and review your efforts to reach it daily. When you score your goal, give each other a high five!

To get everyone involved, consider setting up key result areas (KRA) of activities which will help your goal to be achieved. These KRA tasks can be assigned to different members of your team. These may include internal marketing projects per year, community visits per month, new exams per day, new patient calls per day, follow-up text messages per day, and courtesy visits to referring dental offices. The KRAs could include confirmed new patient records per day, number of new patients scheduled per day, or a patient accommodation each day. Aim high! Celebrate as a team when you achieve your goals.

EXCELLENCE

The quality of a person's life
is in direct proportion to their commitment to excellence,
regardless of their chosen field of endeavor.
– Vince Lombardi

Teams strive to continuously improve. Everything in your dental office has your personal signature on it. This is your office brand. Be the best that you can be in everything that you do. Be a culture in pursuit of excellence. In return, you will build team satisfaction and pride. Excellence in clinical care, outstanding customer service, and a great patient experience are the ultimate team goals.

Chapter 26

A POSITIVE WORKPLACE

When we love our work,
we need not be managed
by hopes of reward
or fears of punishment.
— Warren G. Bennis

W e all want to work in a successful office, where our co-workers are cheerful, effective, and fun, and our patients are well-cared for, happy, and at ease. We want to work with people who are invested in the success of our practice. We want each person to inherently know and feel that "I belong here." There are steps you can take to foster this environment and achieve a positive workplace.

In their book, *First, Break All the Rules*, Marcus Buckingham and Curt Coffman outline results of a Gallup Poll of the important strengths that leading HR executives use to measure excellence in workplace culture. These items, once known and put into place in your dental office, can help to improve the weak areas of employee satisfaction in your office and strengthen team motivation in your workplace culture.

I gave this test to my team at Gorczyca Orthodontics and used the results to improve our level of workplace satisfaction. The outcome surprised me. Our most senior assistant wanted more opportunity for development. Our most organized, task-specific computer-whiz receptionist wanted more direction. This test gave us insight into how we could improve our office culture and *fill individual workplace wants and needs* for the benefit and satisfaction of each person in the office. The fulfillment of workplace desires ultimately improves work engagement, motivation, and happiness. Try giving this test, Factors That Affect Workplace Satisfaction. You too may be surprised and your office improved by the answers.

Grade the following statements on a scale of 1 to 5:

1 - No to 5 - Yes

1. In the last seven days, I have received recognition.
2. In the last six months, my progress has been discussed.
3. This year, I learned and grew.
4. I have the equipment I need to do my best work.
5. My co-workers are committed to quality.
6. I have the opportunity to do my best each day.
7. The mission makes me feel important.
8. My opinions count.
9. I know what is expected of me.
10. Someone at work cares about me as a person.
11. Someone at work encourages my development.
12. I have a best friend at work.

By addressing these findings, you will be giving time to psychological support, encouragement, and welfare of your team. You will be building a more caring and fulfilling work environment.

THE DAILY HUDDLE

Huddles are important to team communication and your ultimate office success. Imagine if all you had were individual, one-on-one talks. No one on the dental team would know what anyone else was doing. No one would know the immediate progress or the long-term goals of the office. This would not be a team. This would be a collection of independent actors.

Imagine an office where team members did not huddle. How would word get out as to changes in the daily schedule? Let's say a sensitive patient was to be seen that day. How would everyone know to provide a little extra TLC? The Huddle also focuses on areas that need more attention, where people can crossover to lend a hand. "That's not in my job description" is something we prefer not to hear at the team Huddle or at any time in a dental practice. Everyone pitches in. Everyone is important.

The Huddle is central to the creation of a positive work environment. At the Huddle, everyone has the ability to express themselves freely; each team member is heard and respected for their opinions; all have the reassurance that they are valued. Beyond the Morning Huddle, activities which build teamwork and member value are the Monthly Team Meeting, and the Annual Advance.

The Monthly Team Meeting

> *Our ability to engage in*
> *passionate, unfiltered debate*
> *about what we need to do to succeed*
> *will determine our future*
> *as much as any products we develop*
> *or partnerships we sign.*
> – Patrick Lencioni

The Monthly Team Meeting is critical for review of team progress. The doctor or HR manager can be the facilitator. Everyone can have the opportunity to speak on behalf of improving the office performance and patient care. The team can work together to come up with new plans for how the office can become more efficient and effective. These collective results represent your score, the success of your dental practice.

Brainstorming is one of the best aspects of the Monthly Team Meeting. Team members know better than anyone else what needs to be done in the dental office. Suggestions on customer satisfaction surveys can also be reviewed. Consider a monthly goal to improve three situations. You can call these the T3s (Trouble X3).

At our orthodontic office, our monthly meeting lasts 90 minutes. Other offices have two monthly team meetings lasting one hour each. Other than beverages, food is not served during this time so the team can *fully focus and be engaged* in the conversation. Laptops are not open. Cell phones are not present. What we want is everyone's full and undivided attention.

Some doctors think they cannot afford the time and cost of semi-monthly or monthly Team Meetings. I think a dentist cannot afford *not* to have a monthly team meeting. This is the time for self-evaluation and 360-degree feedback. It is from here that most great ideas and team unity flow.

If there is "a meeting after the meeting," there is a problem. It means that somehow someone was not able to express their feelings fully, or perhaps the team was not in agreement with decisions that were made. Beware of "the meeting after the meeting." If this happens, try having another Team Meeting to clear the air.

People want the opportunity to speak their minds
and have their ideas, opinions, and feelings heard.
– Jack Welch

ANNUAL ADVANCE

The Annual Advance is an off-site "retreat" in which ideas and plans are advanced. It is an opportunity to plan your office calendar. You may want to have a guest speaker to suggest fresh ideas. You may want to invite a dental coach or consultant. The Advance can be anything that you want it to be. Each year, you can have a different area of focus. Individual Annual Achievement Awards for the past year can be given. A Customer Service Award can be voted on by all members of the team, and given as the highest award possible. In addition to strategic planning for the year ahead, remember, recognize everyone's hard work achievements over the past year.

It's not easy to raise the bar a little every year while continuing to maintain a high-performance standard for your team. A successful team continues to improve. We're all faced with daily challenges. The Annual Advance will give you the perspective to organize solutions, and prevent unwanted events from occurring. Look forward to the opportunity for your employees to improve, using this valuable time to demonstrate what your positive work environment is all about.

Perhaps the first place to start to manage change is with yourself. If you are the doctor, perhaps we might sometimes need to start by saying, "Doctor, the problem is you." As the leader of the team, if the dentist is consistently negative, nasty, or in a bad mood, the chance of a positive work environment is slim. It's important that the dentist-owner remain optimistic and positive, especially in the face of adversity. As the leader, it's important to be disciplined enough to react to difficult situations in an unemotional and productive way. Not only will leadership actions improve the situation, but you will gain the respect of your team.

It's important to be a great boss. What is a great boss? A great boss builds communication while encouraging, developing, and protecting the team. A great boss empowers and builds self-confidence. In this way, a great boss builds trust and respect. All team members should always feel and know that the boss is on their side, and that they are able to express their suggestions of how the office could be improved.

One important thing for leaders to remember is that your team cannot read your mind. It will be necessary to communicate every single action that you desire. Repetition is also needed. Written directives help.

This is where the Team Handbook is extremely useful. Once you've stated the office rules and expectations, document them in the Team Handbook, which should be updated every year. Review the contents regularly. Pay your team members to read the Team Handbook while in office. *Obtain a signed and dated confirmation from each employee which states that they have read and understand the Team Handbook.*

QUARTERLY OUTING

As a team-building exercise for friendship, trust and unity of spirit, spend some time together outside of the office. I can always tell when someone is going to be voluntarily leaving because they don't show up for the unpaid outing. It's predictable. Lack of participation speaks volumes about motivation, enthusiasm and commitment to the organization.

Quarterly events could include bowling, an art studio, a spa day, or lunch. The team that plays together stays together. The doctor may or may not attend. What's important is that this get-together or affair keeps the team energized, builds trust and friendship, and gives everyone something to anticipate. In this way, we become closer. We come to know and count on each other.

Appreciate everything your associates do for the business.
Nothing else can quite substitute
for a few well-chosen, well-timed, sincere words of praise.
They're absolutely free and worth a fortune.
– Sam Walton

APPRECIATION

March 1-7 is National Dental Assistants Appreciation week and June 1-7 is National Orthodontic Assistants Appreciation week. Don't wait until this special time to show your assistants how much you appreciate them. *Take a minute each day, several times per day, to convey recognition.* A simple "Thank you" or "Well done" will do. Tell them up front immediately when they are doing something right. Tell them how good what they did was for the office, how nice it was, or how great it was for the patients, and how much it was appreciated by everyone. Stop for this special moment.

Actions rewarded encourage all team members to do more of the same. Try a victorious high-five once in a while. Maybe a handshake or a thumbs-up would be appropriate. Try a motivational cheer coined by dental consultant Judy Kay of lifting both arms in the air and giving the world a "Ta-Dah!" to excite emotions and lighten the office spirit. Acknowledge team members on a personal level in some way and make the office fun.

When it comes to office results and group achievement, a team cheer is in order. Review the scorecard and if you have surpassed an office goal, it may be time for a bonus. This serves as a reminder that great performance is rewarded and encouraged. This will ensure that this behavior and level of performance is repeated. When the office bottom line is favorable, everyone wins.

Individual achievement deserves recognition. Honor persons who have gone the extra mile. At your Annual Advance, give each awardee a Certificate of Achievement highlighting how they have learned new things and grown in the dental profession throughout the year.

If outstanding care of patients and referring offices is one of your core values, give a Customer Service Award, with a bonus, each year. Team members can vote on this honor. Place the winner's name in the Team Handbook or add their name to a "Wall of Fame" for all to see. I have had several people tell me that their Customer Service Award has been the only award they have ever received. It meant so much to them. It warmed my heart that I could thank them for a job well done, make their family members proud of them, and make them feel a high level of achievement, pride, satisfaction, and happiness.

Tenure achievements deserve special recognition. Surprisingly, the average employee worldwide now stays at a job for only three years. This figure is down from an average of five years twenty years ago.

We celebrate the 5-year milestone with a strand of pearls. For male team members, we would give a watch. These are beautiful gifts, which honorees will cherish forever. Welcome to the dental office "Hall of Fame."

For a 10-year achievement gift, we give a mini-vacation. The team member has certainly earned it.

After 15 years, the assistant is helping to run the practice. They are seasoned stakeholders. For a 15-years achievement award, we give a monetary bonus. Let them buy for themselves what they would most appreciate. It's time for a celebration!

For a 20-year dental veteran, we need to put on our thinking caps to create a remarkable way that this special person can be appreciated for their years of dedication to our office, the doctor, and to the patients we serve. This devotee has perhaps spent more time with you than even your spouse! She can just about read your mind! You know her that well!

Perhaps you will be in a rest home together! The longest tenured dental employee I have ever met was a twenty-seven (27) year veteran in the same office with the same dentist from high school. She stayed with her dentist to the very end. It is possible that your dental assistant may be with you this long or even longer!

The physical gift, although nice, is not as important as the praise and gratitude. Everyone appreciates being honored for his or her achievements. However you reward your employees, do not underestimate the power of recognition.

Human Resources isn't a thing we do.
It's the thing that runs our business.
– Steve Wynn

Strive to be an amazing boss, have an excellent team, and create a positive workplace environment. Design your unique A+ dental utopia to attract and retain employees, to attract the right people gaining satisfaction together through work each and every day.

CASE STUDY 48: "The Amazing Boss"

Dr. V always dreamed of running her own dental practice. She hired an amazing team of professionals whom she genuinely liked, respected, and enjoyed. She then empowered them with time, resources, and the ability to optimize their individual work environment in order to best serve the dental patients.

All contributed. One wanted to decorate the office every season to make it fun for the patients. One wanted to have office uniforms with a logo and a different color for each day of the week. One wanted to start work at 9:30 a.m. in the interests of work-life balance. These ideas were all implemented.

Teamwork was a daily sport. Together, everyone worked hard to attract the right people to join the office and to keep performance standards high. The team participated in active recruitment and was honest when someone was just not a good fit. They expressed their feelings openly and felt comfortable discussing issues that needed to be improved.

Dr. V began daily conversation with the morning huddle, but it didn't stop there. Communication continued throughout the entire day. It was natural for everyone to continuously discuss and work on the schedule. Together, they found creative solutions to make each patient's care flow smoothly throughout the day.

All assistants helped each other for the maximum benefit of the patient. If someone had a few free minutes, they would ask other team members "How can I help you?" No tasks were left undone. The office was clean and ready each evening for the start of the next day. No one was ever alone or deserted in their tasks. Motivation was high. Each day started with a cheerful "Hello" and ended with a fond "Farewell."

Everyone on the team knew and lived the mission and core values of the office. All were committed to excellence and empowered to make changes to improve clinical care, customer service and the patient experience. All were accountable to making constant improvements in an effort to achieve the highest levels of clinical excellence.

Dr. V was committed to education and the personal growth of all employees. Individual achievements were encouraged and rewarded. New leaders rose from within the ranks. Promotions were made. Everyone understood that they were stakeholders in the office, and that the office's success was their shared success.

Dr. V devoted time and resources to valuable events beyond the morning huddle. She did not waste time or money. Meetings were organized and effective. Action items were implemented and reviewed for results. Progress was measured and the team was aligned with clear goals. Performance was rewarded.

The team had a tight loyalty to each other, the doctor, the patients, and the office. They constantly interacted with each other, both inside and outside of the office. They had a high level of trust. Dr. V. asked each person daily how they were doing. The doctor as leader kept each assistant inspired and excited about their work while giving them something special to anticipate. She asked everyone how they were feeling about their work in an effort to foster deep personal satisfaction about their important contributions.

In the end, each team member had a deep sense of personal satisfaction about their job. They were proud of their achievements. They knew that they were in the right office, that what they did mattered, and that they had made a difference in the world.

ACTION:
Be the very best boss you can be. Be open about the performance scorecard. Always remember, it's not about you. When it comes to HR management, it's about them, the team, achieving success together.

Chapter 27

WORK-LIFE BALANCE

Work-life balance is a swap—
a deal you've make with yourself about
what you keep and what you give up.
– Jack Welch

N ext time you're tired, physically sore, and emotionally stressed out from working in your dental office, think about Lillian Moller Gilbreth (1878-1972), the mother of modern business management. Born in Oakland, California, Lillian was a pioneer "superwoman" successfully combining a career with her home life. She did it so well that in 1944 the *California Monthly* called her "a genius in the art of living."

Obtaining her B.A. in literature from UC Berkeley in 1900, she was the first woman to speak at a University of California commencement. She went on to receive her master's degree in literature in 1902 and completed a dissertation to obtain a doctorate from UC in 1911. She was not awarded the degree due to noncompliance with residency. This did not discourage her. Having moved to New England with her family, she went on to attend Brown University where she earned a Ph.D. in 1915, having written a second dissertation in industrial psychology. The first of its type ever given, Lillian received her Ph.D. with her husband and four children at her graduation ceremony.

Lillian, with her husband Frank, went on to found a management-consulting firm. Their company Gilbreth, Inc. pioneered managing the human element. Although he was a bricklayer who never attended college, Frank developed scaffolding and created many motion and efficiency changes in the workplace. Lillian and Frank believed that all aspects of the work environment should be questioned and improvements constantly adopted. The results of the Gilbreth's research lead to changes which diminished fatigue. Their study was the forerunner of ergonomics.

Frank Gilbreth was the first to propose the position of "caddy" for the surgeon. The caddy would hand surgical instruments to the surgeon, improving the efficiency of surgery. It is perhaps Frank Gilbreth who we should thank for creating the concept of four-handed dentistry.

The Gilbreths considered everything down to the smallest detail, including the brightness of the lights in the workplace. Unlike Taylorism, whose management symbol was the stopwatch, the Gilbreth's scientific approach and management theories sought to make processes more efficient by reducing the motions involved. The Gilbreth's first and foremost concern was with workers' welfare and their ability to perform their job well.

In her lifetime, Lillian Gilbreth worked for the Hoover administration and the Truman council. She was instrumental in the development of the modern kitchen and she invented many household items and feminine products. In her lifetime, Lillian earned 23 honorary degrees. She died in 1972 at age 93 while still a resident lecturer at the Sloan School of Business Management at the Massachusetts Institute of Technology.

What's fascinating about Lillian Moller Gilbreth is that she did all of this while still being a wife and mother of twelve children! The Gilbreth family is immortalized in the movie and book "Cheaper by the Dozen" which is how Frank would respond when asked about his twelve children. Lillian Moller Gilbreth truly was a "superwoman."

Can we all be superwomen or supermen? How is it possible to manage so many things in life? We have a family, patients, a dental office, and that still requires time for HR management. I hope that this book has given you the education and organization for implementation of HR time-saving protocols. I hope that this book will improve your time-management skills and help you to make good HR and personal decisions along the way.

Let's eliminate useless, unproductive wastes of time in an effort to enjoy life to the fullest. What's important is to find our own happiness.

Happiness is so important for all aspects of our life, especially for work-life balance. In the work environment, once HR management is mastered and time-wasting situations eliminated, the team will be in sync. You, the dentist, can eliminate sleepless nights and emergency calls to HR experts or attorneys so that you can use this extra time with family and friends. Meanwhile, you will have created a happy workplace, perhaps the dental practice of your dreams. Everyone will be able to say, "Life is good."

DENTIST: THE #1 BEST JOB IN THE U.S.

How does one define the best job? When considering many factors, dental professionals would likely formulate a similar answer, that is, that dentistry is still number one. One factor defining the best job might be great pay with the possibility of growth. Another factor may be reasonable work hours providing for a good work-life balance. A third factor could be an inherent sense of fulfillment and happiness, of doing good work in the world, making people happy, producing something of value, or making the world a better place. A fourth may be a pleasant work environment with a low level of stress. Other factors may include having a sense of pride in one's work and self-respect. We are so fortunate to have all of these in dentistry. This is why *dentistry is often voted the #1 Best Job in the U.S.*

With a comfortable median salary of $146,340 and a comfortable work-life balance, the profession of dentistry has earned the respect of employment and job review agencies year after year. The Bureau of Labor Services (BLS) predicts that dentistry will continue to grow with an additional 23,300 new dentist jobs through the year 2022. The future continues to look bright for dentists and dentistry.

SUICIDE

So, if things are so wonderful in dentistry, the #1 Best Job in the U.S., why then do we continuously hear that dentists have the highest suicide rate of any profession? The *Business Insider* reports that of all careers studied, dentistry was indeed #1 in suicide, with a rate 5.45 times the national average.

Frustration with the intricate manual labor certainly could play a role in the back-room unhappiness of dentistry. Add to this that men are four times more likely to commit suicide than women and that dentistry has until recently been a male-dominated profession, and this could contribute to making this number high. Caucasian Americans are twice as likely to commit suicide as people of color. There are certainly a lot of uptight Caucasians in dentistry.

Starting a new practice is incredibly stressful. In the introduction of my first book *It All Starts with Marketing* I shared that I literally cried the first three months after opening my orthodontic practice from scratch. In dentistry, there are times one may feel alone, hopeless, or trapped in a financially challenging career decision that is not easy to change. During this time, it's important to sit back and remember, "This too shall pass." What's the worst thing that can happen? You can probably declare bankruptcy and move back in with your parents in many cases. What's so bad about that? Your loved ones will certainly be glad to have you and no one will think less of you for it. This certainly beats suicide. Keep your mind clear and realize that everyone has the ability to start over.

Dentists may feel the financial burden in the undertaking of their education and the start-up of a dental practice. The investment of becoming a dentist and owning a dental practice is well worth it. This commitment will ultimately lead you to success and last a long and successful lifetime.

At the start, in mid-career, or even later on, dentists may feel isolation in their practice. They may feel separated away from other professionals or even worse, rejected or in competition with other dentists in their community. Take the time to get to know the other dental professionals in your community. You may be surprised to find friends and colleagues with whom to share your daily challenges. All of your colleagues are facing the exact same professional challenges as you. Reach out for their support or be a friend and lend a hand. There are many wonderful people in dentistry that cannot wait to meet you, help you, and make your dental career fun all along the way.

A good night's sleep is especially important for all healthcare professionals. Some dentists may be working too hard, sleeping too little, and just not enjoying life. Take time to smell the roses. Get out of the dental office as much as you can. Take a break. Go for a walk, work out, listen to music, visit museums, or attend a new dental course. *Work to live, don't live to work.*

All of the patterns mentioned here are symptoms and warning signs of suicide. The good news is, no dentist is alone. *We're all in it together.* Every dentist has gone through the growing pains of starting out in a new dental practice. We are here for each other. This is why I love the message of Howard Farran and Dentaltown which clearly states, "The purpose of Dentaltown is so that no dentist will feel alone or practice alone again." Check it out. Dentaltown provides a great virtual dental community.

Your professional dental organizations also offer mentorship programs at the local, state, and national level. Find the American Dental Association chapter in your community and join it today or become active in your dental and specialty organizations. These are great dental resources. Here you will find and make new friends for life.

My husband has said that I am, personally, "pathologically happy." Other dental professionals may not be so blessed. If you know someone who is struggling in the day-to-day life of being a dentist, be a friend. Visit them. Offer help. Talk to them as much as possible. Remind them of all the wonderful things that they have in their life. Mental illness can be a serious disease. If you or a colleague suffers from depression, seek medical help. Tremendous strides have been made in alleviating the burden and stigma of depression. In the worst-case scenario, remember the National Suicide Prevention Lifeline number, 1-800-273-TALK. Let's make dental suicide a thing of the past.

In the twenty-first century, there is a new type of dentist, the work-life balance dentist. Their focus is not driven foremost by numbers and financial gain but more by a holistic view of life and human happiness. For the first time, these dentists offer work-life balance and choice to their team members as well, many of whom are also wives and mothers, and who also want work-life balance in their own lives.

Dentistry began to discuss the importance of work-life balance in the 1980s when a significant number of women started to enter the dental work force. Often unable to find their first job as a partner, or associate, women dentists and dental specialists tended to open their own practices from scratch, work hard, and thrive financially. Then what happened?

MARRIAGE

In dentistry and in life, one benefits tremendously from having a supportive spouse. This doesn't necessarily mean being married to another dentist or your dental school classmate; it means having someone who supports *your* dental career.

Many dentists delay getting married until they are done with their education. Unless they find the perfect match in high school, college, dental school, or their residency, it may take years for a dentist to find the man or woman of their dreams, if they find them at all. It isn't easy to get married once you are out of dental school. Once working, a dentist's life becomes extremely busy. Free time is at a premium. The dentist's highly respected position in the community can be a hindrance as well. The high standards of single dentists sometime impede dating so that they cannot find someone who they feel is suitable for marriage.

As it turns out, social scientists have established only one fact
about single women's mental health:
employment improves it.
– Susan Faludi

CASE STUDY 49: "THE SINGLE DENTIST"

Thelma and Louise were successful career women. Thelma was a leading businesswoman in the city and Louise was a successful dentist in the suburbs. They both had thriving practices, were professionally involved, and had interesting pastimes. But there was one problem: they were alone. To make matters worse, their biological clocks were ticking.

One night at dinner Thelma stated, "We've got to get serious about finding a husband. We need to be as focused as we were about studies in college, medical school, dental school, and residency. It's time to shift into personal high gear. We've worked very hard on everything else in our lives. At this time, finding our spouse has to be our Number 1 priority!"

The ladies started their search. They joined alumni associations, hiking clubs, bike-a-thons and social groups. They even attended professional baseball games. They told all their friends and professional colleagues that they were interested in finding a boyfriend and getting hitched.

Within one year, both were happily married to successful men. Soon, they cut down on their work hours and career demands to spend more time with their children. They had achieved work-life balance. Life was good.

ACTION:
Being single can be an enjoyable and admirable vocation. But if marriage is a life goal, once out of dental school, matrimony needs to be your top priority. Life is short. The fruits of your labor will be so much sweeter if you have someone special to share them with.

Divorce

If you think paying off your student loans is hard, trying being a successful dental practice owner and getting a divorce after ten years. The Big Five Life Altering Changes are said to be: death of a loved one, loss of a job, loss of a home, major illness, and divorce. The latter can be perhaps the most financially and emotionally devastating to the established dental practitioner.

People change. It is not unusual for an established dentist, who married their high school or college sweetheart to need to sell their practice or to take out a huge bank loan for half the value of their practice as a settlement of divorce. In addition, the working dentist may lose their home to their spouse; they may be encumbered with large child-support payments as well as hefty alimony payments for a lifetime. In many cases, the dentist may not be the instigator of the divorce nor want the divorce at all. Everyone thinks that the disappointment of divorce won't happen to them. I caution you that it can.

As a dentist, you probably have a Living Will and Trust. Think also about preserving your dental practice by having a premarital agreement, prepared by an attorney, to preserve your dental practice and other assets in the case of divorce. A legally prepared and executed premarital agreement, or even a marital agreement, will insure that your practice is off limits in a divorce settlement. Many seasoned dentists, when hiring a younger dental business partner, require a premarital or marital agreement to protect the partnership and the dental practice from any future divorce settlements.

Premarital agreements are easy to create. Your attorney will formulate one for you. The agreement will list all premarital assets and liabilities of both parties. Your fiancé or loved one will also need their own separate attorney to prepare their side of the agreement. It is best to discuss this while dating. There have been many cases when a young successful dentist has asked their fiancé to sign a premarital agreement only to find that their fiancée refused. What does that tell you? The wedding should be called off.

A 2012 study estimated that the lifelong probability of a marriage ending in divorce in the USA is 40-50%. By comparison, the divorce rate of dentists is one of the lowest nationwide at only 7.8%. This divorce rate is close to that of clergy at 5.6%. Physicians and surgeons are slightly higher at 9.2%. Divorce rates of other health professionals are as follows: dental hygienists 14.0%, dental assistants and registered nurses 17.8%, psychologists 19.3%, medical assistants 20.6%.

The balance between work and family affects our day-to-day happiness as well as marital bliss. A 2010 study revealed that a person's job may be one of the best predictors of marriage success or failure. A Navy SEAL's divorce rate is 90-95% while dancers, bartenders, and massage therapists have divorce rates around 40%. We should be thankful that dentistry offers us the benefit of the ability to create work-life balance while maintaining a happy and successful marriage.

FERTILITY

Due to education, career, or just not meeting the right guy, many female dentists who marry and start their families later in life need fertility treatments to have a baby. Many male dentists who marry older women of all professions will be involved in fertility treatments in order to have a child. The female human body is not a refrigerator. Every year that a woman waits to have children, fertility decreases and the chances of chromosomal abnormality grow higher. If you are a female dentist age 35 who wants to start or extend a family, it would be wise to consider ovum preservation right now. Take charge of your biological clock!

Fertility treatments are expensive, generally on the order of $15,000 per cycle. These procedures are usually not paid for by health insurance. When given the opportunity in life, start your family naturally as early as possible. This will not only bring you great joy and fulfillment, it will also save you hundreds of thousands of dollars.

CASE STUDY 50: "THE BIOLOGICAL CLOCK"

June was a forty-two-year-old dental specialist. Recently married, she wanted to have a baby. She knew her chances of getting pregnant naturally at that age were almost zero. June and her fiancé were sufficiently strong in their commitment to one another that they started fertility treatment. She started fertility treatments as soon as she got married.

First, the doctor implanted one embryo. It did not survive. In the next round, the doctor implanted four embryos. They did not survive. It did not appear that the treatments would be successful. Having a friend who had done fertility treatments with success after three tries, June tried a third time. The doctor implanted six embryos. One survived. She gave birth to a healthy baby girl at age 44. It was truly survival of the fittest. She tried to have a second child through fertility management, without avail. In the end, the fertility treatments cost the family $159,000. But the price of having a healthy child was priceless!

ACTION:

If you are a female dentist, hygienist, or dental assistant over the age of thirty-five, or if you are a male dentist married to a woman in that age group and you would like to have children, do not wait one second longer to start your family or start fertility treatments. Remember, the fertility specialists will evaluate both male and female partners. Sometimes men have fertility issues, too. The chances of getting pregnant naturally are less than 50% at age thirty-five. The chances of a woman becoming pregnant naturally will drop to 3% by age forty. Your natural window of childbirth ends by age forty-six.

MATERNITY LEAVE

When you are a female dentist owner in private practice, there are two options for maternity leave substitution: hire an associate to cover your maternity absence or hire a temporary *locum tenens* for the time you plan to be out on maternity leave. The benefits of an associate are that 1: you can introduce them to patients and the dental community ahead of time and 2: you can take as much time as you want for maternity leave. The drawbacks are that 1: the associate may not have enough experience to run your office or make decisions without you there; 2: you *are* telling the patients and the community months in advance that you will be gone which may affect their decision to go elsewhere or not refer family and friends; and 3: an associate is very expensive. Here, the costs may outweigh the benefits.

With *locum tenens*, the dentist is well experienced and often already retired and 2: they already know how to run a practice, and the leave announcement could be held until the time leave starts. Finally, when your leave is short, patients and referring doctors *may not even realize that you have been gone*. There are many important benefits to the *locum tenens* scenario, including peace of mind.

CASE STUDY 51: "THE MATERNITY LEAVE DENTIST"

Dr. Arlene had just had a baby. After twelve hours of labor and a Caesarian section, she lay in her hospital bed with 50 sutures across her abdomen, with her newborn baby and husband by her side.

Then the phone rang. It was her dental office. The front-desk receptionist wanted to know who would be taking the pager home that night. At first Arlene thought, "This must be joke." She replied "The associate, of course." After all, she had hired the associate for an entire year to prepare her for this one day and this time. The receptionist replied, "The doctor won't be in the area tomorrow."

The front-desk receptionist took the pager home overnight. The doctor returned to work one week later and dismissed the associate.

ACTION:
In cases of maternity leave, consider hiring *locum tenens* with career and life experience. If an associate will be replacing you while on maternity leave, *spell out every single detail of your expectations* while you are gone on maternity leave. Don't expect an associate to think or act like a practice owner if they have never before had that experience.

How much are you going to allow work to consume you? Many dentists, both male and female with full-time practices have their spouse at home, full-time. What about a two-career household? Maybe a two-career couple will become so busy professionally that they will choose not to have any children. Women's studies have now shown that the high-functioning career woman *can't* have it all. They can have *a lot*, but they cannot have it *all* and expect to be perfect in every aspect of home life. Either the 50-hour workweek or the homemade dinners prepared by the soccer mom will need to be cut back. Women dentists, like any executives, can be at the top of their field but something in their personal life or professional life will have to be curtailed.

There are some things that physically and biologically only a woman, wife, and mother can do. Giving 100% to your profession and patients means that your marriage and family life are going to receive a little less attention. Perhaps you won't be cooking Friday night dinner for eight or become President of the PTA. Or maybe you'll decide to give up participation in your local dental society or political endeavors in organized dentistry to spend more time helping your child with their homework or practicing a musical instrument. That's O.K. These professional activities can be resumed in "empty nest" years. These are all personal choices. It is for each of us to find our own happiness and to decide what personal work-life balance feels right for us.

You are ultimately responsible for your own happiness and lack thereof. You may decide to give up having children, and to put your career first. Just remember that your decisions have ramifications. Your spouse will also be affected by the choices that you make and your team will also need to live and work by your work schedule and style of work-life balance.

When dentists have a choice in life, there are many benefits to having children first and concentrating more on your practice later in life. You only get one chance in your life to have biological children. As far as your practice is concerned, you have the rest of your life.

Female dentists who are wives and mothers can share family concerns with their team members who also understand family obligations. I once read a discussion about team members who consistently showed up late for work. I thought, "My team members *NEVER* come late for work." Why is that? Could it be because we start most days at 9:30 a.m.?

Getting kids to school and starting work at 8:00 or 8:30 a.m. is quite a daunting task for a working mother. Anyone who has ever gotten a young child ready for school in the morning knows that it is not easy and that it can often be unpredictable. Not rushing for the 8:15 a.m. drop-off time is quite a luxury and easily attained by starting work at 9:30 a.m. Getting to school is hard enough without adding the rush to work. As a working mother, all of our time with children is precious. Let's make it all non-rushed, quality time.

Your attention to work-life balance may determine how desirable your dental office is as a place of employment. Everyone wants life to feel in balance. For example, a mother with four children and a husband who works is not going to last long in an office that starts work every day at 7:00 a.m., with a 40+ hour work week, including Saturdays. Conversely, a highly competitive, money-driven dental boss is probably not going to keep well-balanced team members with high family priorities for very long.

How far should the work-life balance scales be tipped? Should you allow team members to leave work early to watch their son's baseball game? When taken as a vacation or personal day off with eight weeks' notice, a special event request is reasonable. When asked to alter a weekly work schedule in order to accommodate recurring requests, for this the answer is usually no.

Only a superstar with an incredible performance and long-term tenure might be worth special exceptions. You cannot make special arrangements that would hurt the practice on a continuous basis. This practice is risky but sometimes necessary to keep top-quality people. All team members, with or without children, need to be treated with fairness. What you can offer each team member is a balanced place to work, where team members are challenged but not stressed and overworked, and vacations and personal days are taken regularly by all, including the doctor. This is a healthy work environment.

A supportive organizational culture where flexibility exists will keep great team members longer. Mothers of dental patients enjoy speaking to other mothers who are members of your dental team about life and activities in the local community. Patients love to feel and share in the good vibes of office contentment.

CHILDREN

It is up to each dentist and team member to work out her own child-care support and family routine to mesh with that of the dental office. Work-life balance is for the individual to solve, not the office. Personal problems cannot come to work. Working dentists, hygienists, and dental auxiliaries will most often need a devoted spouse or nanny to help with their schedule and childcare. Once home, all of us are best to compartmentalize work and not think or discuss the office. Let it rest. Home is especially not the place to think about HR management issues. Home is where the heart is. Bring home a smile.

Learn to Say "No"

Many volunteer activities can take over a dentist's life. When feeling stretched thin, unhappy, or stressed-out, this is the most important time to learn to say "no." At these times, your extra activities need to be re-examined. These opportunities could include national and international meetings, the local dental society, volunteer teaching, charity work, coaching, or lecturing. Learning to say "no" will give you more quality time in the most important areas of your life. Learning to say "no" may also increase a dentist's personal achievement and professional success. And on those occasions when you do say "yes," your colleagues will respect your selective commitment even more.

Evaluate your own happiness. Take time to schedule some "me" time in solitude to think. This is hard but necessary for your own personal health, happiness, and career longevity.

Dentists can easily become workaholics, addicted to work or perhaps even money. Being a workaholic can also be associated with perfectionist behavior and obsessive compulsion. There's a little of that in dentistry. I actually knew a dentist once who slept overnight in his office! If you do not have the intrinsic desire to go home at night, even if you are single, something may be missing from your personal life. Being a workaholic can be a sign of something more, a negative situation. If this is the case, change the situation and get some help.

Experience: that most brutal of teachers.
But you learn,
my God, do you learn.
– C. S. Lewis

I've been in dentistry a long time, now over 25 years. I've known a lot of dentists, I've observed a lot of dentists, I've seen dentists come and go, and I've witnessed their behaviors. One thing I know for sure, the size of your practice does not necessarily determine your overall financial success or your ultimate state of happiness. This has been true of my own situation as well as that of many other dentists. I knew one dentist whose practice grew so large, so fast, that she felt she had no choice but to sell it and move to a smaller, more remote community to re-find her own happiness.

I once had lunch with an ambitious dentist. When we started to talk, the first thing he told me was that his practice grossed 3 million dollars a year. He employed eight general dentists and specialists and had a huge team of support staff. They worked six days per week including Saturdays and took a lot of dental plans.

I then asked him, "What is your profit margin and net salary?" A bit shocked, he replied that his profit margin was 8% and his annual take-home was $150,000.

Wouldn't it be better to run a solo practice with lower gross receipts but higher yield? Wouldn't it be better to work four days per week, gross $800,000 and earn $350,000? For those running dental groups or working in large dental chains, wouldn't it be better to have equity in your own practice, while enjoying personal freedom? These are the questions each of us needs to ask and answer ourselves. We have the power to choose how we run our own careers, practices, and our lives.

The most that can be said of flattery
is that it is sometimes a cheap psychological trick
with which charlatans and dishonest people
lull others into a state of carelessness
while they pick their pockets.
– Napoleon Hill

CASE STUDY 52: "THE HAPPY DENTIST"

Dr. Joe was a dentist earning a lot of money. His take-home salary was $982,000 per year. He worked five days per week in his private practice. In his free time, he would ride his motorcycle, run 10K races, lift weights, and attend community events. He had few worries except one—he was a workaholic and alone.

Then came marriage. Joe married a beautiful and supportive woman and had four children. Suddenly, work and his hobbies didn't seem so all-consuming. He became a family man. He cut his workweek down to four days per week so that he could have at least one day at soccer practice with the kids. He cut back on his personal sports and he gained a little extra weight. He earned less money but he and his family were happy and had free time to enjoy life together doing things they loved. Life was good.

His financial advisor was somewhat of a yes woman. He found her often agreeing with everything he would say. The advisor was often unprepared for meetings. When Joe would ask about practical courses of action, the responses would be, "Why bother, everything is perfect," and "What recession?" The meetings started to seem pointless. Reports started to have errors. There was just a continuous push in an attempt to sell unmanaged mutual funds.

Then Joe's father died. Although this had been discussed with the advisor, there was not a card or even a word of sympathy before the advisor asked how she could invest Joe's inheritance. Joe and his family felt so disconnected at that point and he could no longer trust this advisor, who acted as if all she wanted was to extract his wealth.

Joe switched to an advisor who considered his personal and family's happiness and quality of life as a top priority. His new advisor was brutally honest in all aspects of his practice and financial affairs. She acknowledged what was important to Joe and told him it was her job to take great care of him, his business, his financial affairs, his wife, and his family. She put thought into Joe's future and gave him a 27-step action plan outlining the anticipated steps to his future retirement.

Joe was at peace. He now had total confidence in the decision he had made and in those with whom he was working. His practice grew and his family thrived. Life was once again good. Joe was the richest man in the world.

ACTION:

It's sad at times when dentists work with people who care so little about them and so much about themselves and their own financial gain. As dentists, we are constantly bombarded by businessmen and salespeople of all types. It is a continuous question of who to work with, who to trust, who can contain confidentiality, and where we should spend our money to get value and performance from the services we seek and pay for as the customer.

Beware of sycophants and Yes Men in all aspects of dentistry. They are common. This could apply to advisors or salesman selling a new product. Flattery is often used to hook dentists into a new business decision. Some also use fear tactics. We need to be aware of this presence in our profession of dentistry and our tendency to not critically evaluate every situation. Think carefully about those with whom you work and the business dealings which affect you. Be sure to evaluate every option and to ask other dentists about their experiences and advice.

Asking for personal referrals from other dentists to firms you can trust is critical in dentistry. This is, after all, your only life and the career you have worked so hard to achieve, and you want to make smart choices. Seek out and hire and pay trusted advisors and coaches to help *you*, not themselves. Be sure that your advisors have action plans for your success as opposed to the sole purpose being the padding of their own wallets. Look for candid feedback from someone who is on your side. Re-evaluate and make good decisions. Change in a positive direction is always good. Don't be afraid of switching advisors. Take time to ask yourself what would make you happy. Keep life good.

> *Not I, nor anyone else can travel that road for you.*
> *You must travel it by yourself.*
> *It is not far. It is within reach.*
> – Walt Whitman

In the end, you are your own best personal consultant. Learn what you can from the best in your field, and from those recommended by other dentists. Then implement what is best for you personally. Check into the background, education, and experience of your advisors in dentistry. Consider whether their values match your own. This is especially true as we begin to approach a time when fifty percent of the dental force is women. Do the firms with whom you work have women in leadership positions? What are their views of women in the workforce? If they have no women in their own firm, what makes you think they will be devoted to your success as a woman professional?

In her book *Lean In*, Sheryl Sandberg discusses the challenges of being a working mother and having a full life. She laments that not enough women reach the top of the corporate world. I think not enough women dentists reach the top in the dental world. Indeed, if you look at the publication "Top Women in Dentistry" very few of the women pictured are even dentists! What's up with that? Where are the women dentists? Is someone else running the "women in dentistry" profession? Sandberg urges women to "take a seat at the table, keep your hand up, and stay engaged." I agree.

We have so much to be thankful for in dentistry: the ability to help others, creative work, a great office environment, excellent teams, great hours, and the ability to earn a good living. Whatever your position in dentistry, be grateful for being a part of the caring dental profession. We're all in it together. And, dentistry is a wonderful place to be. It is still a privilege to be a dentist.

CONCLUSION

Success is turning knowledge into positive action.
– Dorothy Leeds

I hope that this book about Human Resource Management will help you in many ways. Your increased awareness of situations that may arise in your dental office and in your life will help you to conquer future challenges. After reading this book, I hope you will be able to better handle HR situations with finesse. You now know you are not alone in your daily challenges. I hope that having read this book will contribute to your professional joy and happiness.

Human Resource Management is about people. It requires a leader. That leader is you. It requires courage, communication, and candor. Just remember: in HR management, it's about them, your team members, and their personal and professional growth and performance. It's about nurturing, analyzing situations, and taking action, not only with your team but also with yourself.

We can do no great things, only small things with great love.
– Mother Theresa

Human Resource Management is like a train. The train keeps moving town to town. People get on and people get off. The conductor never changes. The conductor is you, the dentist, the manager, the director of HR. The conductor's job never ends. It just goes on and on. So, go on and lead. Most of all, have fun. Enjoy the ride beyond the morning huddle.

Appendix 1

HR CALENDAR TEMPLATE

	Individual	Team	Law
Jan			
Feb			
Mar			
Apr			
May			
June			
July			
Aug			
Sept			
Oct			
Nov			
Dec			

Appendix 2

SAMPLE HR CALENDAR

	Individual	Team	Law
Jan	Achievement awards	Annual team advance	Post IPP incident report
Feb	Update procedure manuals	Review vacation calendar	Update Dr.'s license
Mar	Team member recognition	Quarterly team outing	CE State Law
Apr	Cross-training development	Office cleanup	Update OSHA
May	Project updates	Workplace evaluation	Update HIPAA
June	Mid-year one-on-one	Quarterly team outing	CE CPR
July	Survey patient reviews	Review service standards	Update office manual
Aug	Update uniforms	Attitude assessment	Review safety
Sept	CE management meeting	Quarterly team outing	Review leave policies
Oct	Progress review	Cross-training	Review social media policy
Nov	Coming year projects	Leadership evaluation	Review harassment
Dec	Raises and bonuses	Quarterly team outing	Update wage poster

ACKNOWLEDGEMENTS

Namaste.
I honour the place in you
where the entire universe resides.
A place of light, of love,
of truth, of peace, of wisdom.
I honour the place in you where
when you are in that place
and I am in that place
there is only one of us.
– Mohandas K. Gandhi

Books are built over time. This resource has been a personal labor of passion for the creation of dental resources. It is the result of numerous years in clinical practice, experiences, conversations, classes, resources and collaboration among my colleagues and friends who care about orthodontics, dentistry, human resource management, and dental practice management. Thanks to all of you for sharing your thoughts and experiences with me.

I am thankful to the people who made this book possible. Thank you to the excellent team at Gorczyca Orthodontics without whom patient care and HR activities would not exist: Jolene, Monica, Veronica, Patti, and Gwen. Thank you to all who have worked with us over the years and been part of our office culture and fun team.

Thank you to Marianne Way for the initial transcription of this manuscript.

Thank you to my dear friend Dr. Maureen Valley, of Valley Orthodontics, San Rafael, California who was my classmate at both Harvard School of Dental Medicine and the Harvard School of Public Health. Your passion for dental practice management and organization of the Practice Management course at the Arthur A. Dugoni School of Dentistry, University of the Pacific gave birth to first a lecture, then a presentation, then this book.

Thank you to Bruce Tulgan for his friendship and inspiration, also for his incredible books in the field of human resource management, and for writing the introduction to this book.

My heartfelt gratitude to all the great minds and people who helped me in the writing of this book. Thank you to Attorney Art Curley who has given of himself so generously in years of service to the dentists of Northern California. Thank you for your insights into legal aspects of HR management.

A big thank you to David Harris of Prosperident for his dedicated and insightful guidance in the area of dental embezzlement. It was insightful, eye opening and at times shocking to share your knowledge and experiences pertaining to the dark side of HR management. Thank you for your exceptional enthusiasm and support in the writing of this book.

Thank you to John McGill for your amazing analytic skills, candor, guidance and advice for both my family and me. Thank you for your valuable and insightful feedback on the issues of employment law and for your support of the writing of this book.

Thank you to Paul Edwards, CEDR Solutions HR for your passion for HR management. Your insightful comments and blogs, and interesting conversations have helped to clarify many topics in this book as well as keep them safe within the boundaries of advisable HR practices.

A deep heartfelt thank you to Barbara Freet of Human Resource Advisors, Lafayette, California. You continue to be my closest HR mentor, colleague and friend for over twenty-five years. Somehow, you have managed to make every aspect of HR a fun and most memorable adventure! I appreciate all the time that we have spent together both in and outside of the office passionately discussing HRM.

Thank you to Dr. Wayne Pernell, best-selling and award-winning author and high-performance leadership enhancement coach. I appreciate and treasure your positivity, optimism, humor, and advice into the psychology of HR solutions. Your insight has been inspiring and invaluable.

Thank you to HR Attorney Ali Oromchian and to Andrew Llama from HR for Health for your organizational insight and guidance with the legal aspects of HR management.

Thank you to Linda Boyd, Director of Diablo Valley College Dental Assisting Program, Concord, California for providing desirable work behavior, well-trained dental interns and dedicated team members to our office for twenty-five years. Your graduates have always been, and continue to be, pillars of professionalism.

Thank you to Howard Farran for your contributions and unique creativity in the field of dental practice management. Your enthusiasm and love of dentistry through Farran Media, Dentaltown and Orthotown Magazines is unsurpassed. Thank you for your support, encouragement, and contribution towards the creation of this book.

Thank you to orthodontist Dr. Donna Galante of The Galante Group for her enthusiasm and business management contributions to the field of dentistry. Your continued dedication to others and the profession of orthodontics, women orthodontists, and dentistry is a bright light which makes a difference.

Thank you to my publisher Stephanie Chandler of Authority Publishing, and Sue Canfield, project manager, for their assistance and advice in the writing of my second book.

Thank you to my sister Diane Gorczyca Patrick, M.D., for your insights from the field of medicine.

Thank you to my loving husband for his brilliant and dedicated editorial work necessary to help me get this project completed and this book done. All my love to my husband Richard and my son Richard, who share my writing adventures with me every step of the way with curiosity, wonder, patience, forbearance, and love.

Thank you to all of you who have purchased this book and read it to the end.

Ann Marie Gorczyca, D.M.D., M.P.H., M.S.
The Sea Ranch, California

ABOUT THE AUTHOR

Human resource management takes
courage, communication, and candor.
– Ann Marie Gorczyca

D r. Ann Marie Gorczyca is a Clinical Adjunct Professor of Orthodontics at the Arthur A. Dugoni School of Dentistry, University of the Pacific, where she teaches practice management. Human resource management is the sixth lecture of a six-part series that includes marketing, teamwork, treatment coordination, customer service, systems management and human resource management.

Dr. Gorczyca is a Diplomate of the American Board of Orthodontics, a member of the Angle Society of Orthodontists, and a graduate of Advanced Education in Orthodontics (Roth Course). She is a member of the Seattle Study Club, the American Association of Orthodontists (AAO), the Pacific Coast Society of Orthodontists (PCSO), the California Association of Orthodontists (CAO), the American Dental Association (ADA), the California Dental Association (CDA), and the Contra Costa Dental Society. She was an orthodontic associate of Dr. T. M. Graber in Evanston, Illinois. She has worked in a multispecialty group practice in Fairfield, California, and she has been a practicing orthodontist in Antioch, California for twenty-five years.

Dr. Gorczyca graduated from Wellesley College, the Harvard School of Dental Medicine, the Harvard School of Public Health and Northwestern University. She has studied at the Harvard School of Public Health's Department of Health Management and Policy; she holds a Master's in Public Health. She is active in her local dental community with the American Association of Dental Office Managers (AADOM). She also served on the AAO Council of Communications, and ADA National Boards Part II Test Construction Committee. She is presently Treasurer of the Northern California Angle Society and serves as a Board Member for the Pacific Coast Society of Orthodontists.

Dr. Gorczyca is the author of *It All Starts with Marketing—201 Marketing Tips for Growing a Dental Practice*. She was a marketing speaker at the 2011, 2012, and 2014 American Association of Orthodontists Annual Sessions and in 2015 on the topic of this book, *Beyond the Morning Huddle—HR Management for a Successful Dental Office*.

She lives in Walnut Creek and The Sea Ranch, California with her husband and son. This is her second book.

BIBLIOGRAPHY

Abrashoff, Captain D. Michael. *It's Our Ship.* New York, Business Plus, 2008.

Abrashoff, Captain D. Michael. *It's Your Ship.* New York, Business Plus, 2001.

Bazerman, Max H. *The Power of Noticing.* New York, Simon & Schuster, 2014.

Blanchard, Ken, Johnson, Spencer. *The One Minute Manager.* New York, HarperCollins, 2003.

Buckingham, Marcus, Coffman, Curt. *First, Break All the Rules.* New York, Simon & Schuster, 1999.

Carnegie, Dale. *How to Win Friends and Influence People.* New York, Pocket Books, 1982.

Christensen, Clayton M. *How Will You Measure Your Life?* New York, HarperCollins Publishers, 2012.

Covey, Stephen R. *The 7 Habits of Highly Effective People: Powerful Lessons in Personal Change.* New York, Free Press, 2004.

Daum, Kevin. *10 Things Really Amazing Bosses Do.* Inc. Magazine, April 2, 2013, online.

Devine, George. *Managing Your Employees.* Englewood Cliffs, Prentice Hall, 1997.

Edwards, Mark R., Ewen, Ann J. *360 Degree Feedback,* New York, Amacom, 1996.

Edwards, Paul. *http://www.cedrsolutions.com/exempt-vs-non-exempt-status/. Exempt vs. Non-Exempt Status: It's More Than Just Salary.* 2014.

Edwards, Paul. *http://www.cedrsolutions.com/nlrb-no-gossiping. The NLRB Hates Your No Gossiping Policy. Here's Why.* February 24, 2015.

Epley, Nicholas. *Mindwise.* Reprint. New York, Vintage Books, 2015.

Espinoza, Chip, Ukleja, Mick, Rusch, Craig. *Managing the Millennials.* Hoboken, John Wiley & Sons, 2010.

Follett, Mary Parker. *Dynamic Administration.* New York, Harper & Brothers, 1940.

Friedman, Stewart D., *Leading the Life You Want.* Boston, Harvard Business Review Press, 2014.

Friedman, Stewart D., *Total Leadership.* Boston, Harvard Business Review Press, 2008.

Forni, P.M. *The Thinking Life.* New York, St. Martin's Press, 2011.

Fredrickson, Barbara L. *Positivity.* New York, MJF Books, 2009.

Gitomer, Jeffrey. *Little Gold Book of Yes! Attitude.* Upper Saddle River, FT Press, 2006.

Goldstein, Valerie Hope. *Employment Law.* Deerfield Beach, E-Z Legal Forms, Inc. 1995.

Goleman, Daniel. *Emotional Intelligence.* New York, Bantam Dell, 1995.

Goleman, Daniel. *Working with Emotional Intelligence.* New York, Bantam Dell, 1998.

Heathfield, Susan M. *What Makes a Bad Boss - Bad?* About.com About Money (2015) online.

Hong, S. Mark. *Power Dressing for the Dentist.* Dental Economics, (2014), (11) online.

http://www.hhs.gov/healthcare/rights/ About the Law/ HHS.gov/health-care. Assist. Sec./Public Affairs *November* 14, 2014.

http://betterlifecoachingblog.com/2010/10/21/dont-let-the-tail-wag-the-dog/ Don't Let the Tail Wag the Dog. October 21, 2010.

http://www.dol.gov/dol/topic/retirement/erisa.htm Employee Retirement Income Security Act (ERISA) U.S Department of Labor - Find It By Topic - Retirement Plans, Benefits & Savings - ERISA

http://www.inc.com/encyclopedia/cross-training.html – Cross-Training

http://en.wikipedia.org/wiki/Lilly_Ledbetter – Lilly Ledbetter

http://en.wikipedia.org/wiki/Mary_Parker_Follett – Mary Parker Follett - Wikipedia, the free encyclopedia.

https://www.sdsc.edu/ScienceWomen/gilbreth.html – Lillian Moller Gilbreth: Mother of Modern Management.

http://womenshistory.about.com/od/business/p/m_p_follett.htm – Mary Parker Follett-Management Pioneer and Theorist.

Hyman, Jon. *Tread Lightly if Banning Workplace Gossip, Warns NLRB Judge, http://www.workforce.com/blogs/3-the-practical-employer/*

post/20191-tread-lightly-if-banning-workplace-gossip-warns-nlrb-judge. January 8, 2014.

Kelloway, E., Loughlin, C., Barling, J. and Nault, A. "Self-Reported Counter-Productive Behaviors and Organizational Citizenship Behaviors." *International Journal of Selection and Assessment, 10,* 143–151, 2002.

Krzyzewski, Mike, Spatola, Jamie K. *Beyond Basketball*, New York, Business Plus, 2006.

Landry, Miles, et. al. Patient Preference for Doctor Attire: *The White Coat's Place in the Medical Profession.* Ochsner J. Fall; 13(3): 334–342, 2013.

Lencioni, Patrick. *http://www.inc.com/magazine/201504 How to Grow by Cutting Back* Inc.com, 2015.

Lencioni, Patrick. *The Advantage.* San Francisco, Jossey-Bass, 2012.

Lencioni, Patrick. *The Five Dysfunctions of a Team.* San Francisco, Jossey-Bass 2002.

Lepsinger, Richard, Lucia, Anntoinette D. *The Art and Science of 360 Degree Feedback.* 2nd ed. San Francisco, Pfeiffer, 2009.

Mitchell, Barbara, Gamlem, Cornelia. *The BIG BOOK of HR.* Pompton Plains, New Jersey, Career Press, 2012.

Miles, Linda. *Dynamic Dentistry.* Virginia Beach, Virginia, Link Publishing, 2003.

Nelson, Bob, Economy, Peter. *The Management Bible.* Hoboken, John Wiley & Sons, 2005.

Patterson, Kerry, Grenny, Joseph, Maxfield, David, McMillan, Ron, Switzler, Al. *Crucial Accountability.* 2nd ed. New York, McGraw-Hill, 2013.

Patterson, Kerry, Grenny, Joseph, McMillan, Ron, Switzler, Al. *Crucial Conversations.* New York, McGraw-Hill, 2002.

Peters, Tom, Austin, Nancy. *A Passion for Excellence: The Leadership Difference.* New York, Grand Central Publishing, 1989.

Peters, Tom. *The Little BIG Things.* New York, HarperCollins Publishers, 2010.

Robbins, Stephen P., and Judge, Timothy A. *Essentials of Organizational Behavior.* 11th ed. Upper Saddle River, New Jersey, Prentice Hall, 2011.

Salzberg, Sharon. *Real Happiness at Work.* New York, Workman Publishing, 2013.

Schwerdtfeger, Patrick. *Make Yourself Useful.* Lulu.com, 2008.

Seligman, Martin E. P. *Learned Optimism.* Reprint. New York, Vintage Books, 2006.

Sember, Brette McWhorter, Sember, Terrence J. *Bad Apples.* Avon, Adams Business, 2009.

Tulgan, Bruce. *H. O. T. Management.* Amherst, HRD Press, 2004.

Tulgan, Bruce. *It's Okay To Be the Boss.* New York, HarperCollins Publishers, 2007.

Tulgan, Bruce. *Not Everyone Gets a Trophy.* San Francisco, Jossey-Bass, 2009.

Tulgan, Bruce. *The 27 Challenges Managers Face.* San Francisco, Jossey-Bass, 2014.

Tulgan, Bruce. *Winning the Talent Wars.* New York, W. W. Norton & Company, 2001.

Ulrich, Dave, Younger, Jon, Brockbank, Wayne, Ulrich, Mike. *HR from the OUTSIDE IN.* New York, McGraw-Hill, 2012.

Weinschenk, Susan M. *How to Get People to Do Stuff.* New Riders, USA, 2013.

Welch, Jack & Suzy. *The Real-Life MBA.* New York, HarperCollins, 2015.

Welch, Jack & Suzy. *WINNING.* New York, HarperCollins, 2005.

Williams, Roy, Crothers, Tim. *Hard Work.* Chapel Hill, Algonquin Books, 2009.

Winfrey, Oprah. *What I Know for Sure.* New York, Hearst Communications, 2014.

Wooden, John, Jamison, Steve. *Wooden.* New York, McGrawHill, 1997.

INDEX

CPSIA information can be obtained
at www.ICGtesting.com
Printed in the USA
BVOW06*1828160517
484041BV00005B/40/P

9 781935 953685